Mockingbird Flight

Patricia Haglund Nielsen
Floyd Sucher
Charlotte G. Garman

THE ECONOMY COMPANY
Oklahoma City   Indianapolis   Los Angeles

ISBN 0-8332-1707-0

ACKNOWLEDGMENTS

For permission to adapt and reprint copyrighted materials, grateful acknowledgment is made to the following:

Allyn and Bacon, Inc., for "The Old and the New" by Q.B.M. from *The Sound of Poetry* by Mary C. Austin and Queenie B. Mills, © copyright 1963 by Allyn and Bacon, Inc. Reprinted by permission of Allyn and Bacon, Inc.

Flossie Arnold, for "O My Little Boy" and "Feeding Time" ("Little Girl"), used by permission. The University of Alabama Press © 1950.

Board of Jewish Education, Inc., New York, NY, for the courtesy of permitting the inclusion of "Havenu Shalom Aleichem" and "My Dreydl."

Bowmar/Noble Publishers, Inc., for "The Children's Zoo," "Someday Very Soon," and "How Many Raindrops?" from *The Small Singer* by Roberta McLaughlin and Lucille Wood, copyright © 1969 by Bowmar/Noble Publishers, Inc.; for "Let's Build a House," "Fire Song," "Sailing Song," "Beauty in the World," "Little Baby Chicks," and "Green Rose Hula" from *Sing a Song of People* by Roberta McLaughlin and Lucille Wood, copyright © 1973 by Bowmar/Noble Publishers, Inc.; for "My Hands," "Ten Little Frogs," "Little Pilgrims," "Ten Little Jingle Bells," "Magic Time," and "If You Were a Farmer" from *Singing Fun* by Lucille F. Wood and Louise B. Scott, © 1954; and for "I'm Not Scared" and "Mother Goose Lullaby" from *More Singing Fun* by Lucille F. Wood and Louise B. Scott, © 1961, all used by permission of Bowmar/Noble Publishers, Inc.

Curtis Brown, Ltd., for "It Rained a Mist," copyright 1948 by Ruth Crawford Seeger, and for "Animal Song," copyright © 1950 by Ruth Crawford Seeger, both reprinted by permission of Curtis Brown, Ltd.

Cooperative Recreation Service, Inc., Delaware, Ohio, for the courtesy of permitting the inclusion of "After School," "Kum Ba Yah," "Kuckuck," and "My Farm."

Thomas Y. Crowell, Publishers, for lyrics and melody of "Let's Go Walking" and melody of "There Was a Little Turtle" from *Another Singing Time: Songs for Nursery and School* by Satis N. Coleman and Alice G. Thorn, copyright 1937 by Satis N. Coleman and Alice G. Thorn, renewed 1965 by Walter B. Coleman, Dr. Charles H. Coleman, and Linton S. Thorn, a John Day Book, "My Rocket Ship" from *The Sunflower Songbook* by June Norton, © 1935, 1956, 1963 by June Mary Norton and Charlotte Byj, a John Day Book, and lyrics and melody for "Pony Song" from *Singing Time: Songs for Nursery and School* by Satis N. Coleman and Alice G. Thorn, copyright 1929 by Satis N. Coleman and Alice G. Thorn, renewed 1957 by Satis N. Coleman and Horace E. Thorn, a John Day Book, all by permission of Thomas Y. Crowell, Publishers.

Deseret Book, Salt Lake City, Utah, for the courtesy of permitting the inclusion of "Smiles," "When We're Helping," "Popcorn Popping," and "Give, Said the Little Stream," all reprinted from *Sing with Me.*

Doubleday & Company, Inc., and The Society of Authors as the literary representative of the Estate of Rose Fyleman, for "Singing-Time" from *The Fairy Green* by Rose Fyleman, copyright 1923 by George H. Doran Co. Reprinted by permission of Doubleday & Company, Inc., and The Society of Authors.

Follett Publishing Company, for "Whirlybird" by Margaret Fullerton from *Music Round About Us*, copyright © 1964 by Follett Publishing Company; for "A Basketful of Nuts" from *Music Through the Year*, copyright © 1963, previous copyright © 1956, 1957, 1959 by Follett Publishing Company, both used by permission of Follett Publishing Company, a division of Follett Corporation; and for the courtesy of permitting the inclusion of "The First Tulip," "Dance with Me," "Looby Loo," "The Railroad Train," and "Are You Sleeping?" from their Elementary music series.

Free to Be Foundation, for "Free to Be . . . You and Me" by Stephen Lawrence and Bruce Hart from *Free to Be . . . You and Me,* 1974, McGraw-Hill Book Company, Inc., New York. Used by permission of the Free to Be Foundation, Inc.

General Music Publishing Company, Inc., for "Little White Duck," © 1950 General Music Publishing Co., Inc.

Ginn and Company, for "Who Are You?" and the music for "Here Is the Beehive" from *The Kindergarten Book* of Our Singing World series, © copyright 1959, 1957, 1949 by Ginn and Company (Xerox Corporation); for the words and melody of "Clapping Game" from *Singing Every Day* of Our Singing World series, © copyright 1959, 1957, 1950 by Ginn and Company (Xerox Corporation); for "The Bus" and "Taking Off" from *Piano Accompaniments for Singing on Our Way* of Our Singing World series, © copyright 1959, 1949 by Ginn and Company (Xerox Corporation); and for "One More River" and "The Animal Fair" from *Piano Accompaniments for Singing Together* of Our Singing

World series, © copyright 1959, 1951 by Ginn and Company (Xerox Corporation); all selections used with permission.

Harvard University Press, for "Who's That?" Reprinted by permission of the publishers from *On the Trail of Negro Folk-Songs* by Dorothy Scarborough. Copyright 1925 by Harvard University Press; 1953 by Mary McDaniel Parker.

Holt, Rinehart and Winston, Inc., for "Wind through the Olive Trees" from Boardman and Landis: *Exploring Music, Book 2,* copyright © 1971, permission by courtesy of Holt, Rinehart and Winston, Inc., publishers.

The Instructor Publications, Inc., for "Early Morning at the Zoo" by Helen M. Webster, reprinted from *Instructor,* August/September 1974, copyright © 1974 by The Instructor Publications, Inc., and "Ping-Pong" by Mary E. Brougher, reprinted from *Instructor,* August/September 1977, copyright © 1977 by The Instructor Publications, Inc. Both used by permission.

Stephen Lehmer, for "Indian Lullaby" from *Seven Indian Songs* by Dr. Derrick Lehmer. Reprinted by permission of Mr. Stephen Lehmer.

J. B. Lippincott, Publishers, for an excerpt from "Ring around the World" in *All Through the Year* by Annette Wynne, copyright 1932, © renewed 1960 by Annette Wynne. Reprinted by permission of J. B. Lippincott, Publishers.

Macmillan Publishing Company, Inc., for the text of "I Had a Little Turtle," reprinted with permission of Macmillan Publishing Co., Inc., from *Collected Poems* by Vachel Lindsay, copyright 1920 by Macmillan Publishing Co., Inc., renewed 1948 by Elizabeth C. Lindsay; Macmillan Publishing Company, Inc., and Hamish Hamilton Ltd., British publishers, for "Bees" from *Toucans and Other Poems* (British title *Zoo Doings and Other Poems*) by Jack Prelutsky, copyright © 1970 by Jack Prelutsky.

National Museum of Canada, Ottawa, for "Eskimo Dance Song" from *Songs of the Copper Eskimos, Report of Arctic Expedition 1913-1918,* by Roberts and Jenness, Ottawa, Canada, 1925.

Patricia T. Pinkston, for "A Lizard and a Frog," words and music by Patricia T. Pinkston.

Plymouth Music Company, Inc., for permission to reprint "Hello, Ev'rybody," "Marching Song," and "I Can't Spell Hippopotamus."

G. Schirmer, Inc., for "Eency-weency Spider," "Where Is Thumbkin?" and "Johnny Works with One Hammer," all selections copyright 1955 by G. Schirmer, Inc., and "The Birch Tree" from the *Botsford Collection of Folk Songs, Volume 2,* G. Schirmer, Inc., publisher and copyright owner. All used by permission.

Simon and Schuster, Inc., for "Come On and Join In to The Game," "Who Did?" and "The Fox and the Goose," all selections copyright © 1966 by Marie Winn and Allan Miller and reprinted by permission of Simon & Schuster, a Division of Gulf & Western Corporation.

University of Nebraska Press, for the courtesy of permitting the inclusion of "Sandy Land," reprinted from *American Play-Party Songs* by B. A. Botkin (*University of Nebraska Studies,* 1937) by permission of University of Nebraska Press.

The Willis Music Company, for "Good Night" from *Music Is Motion* © The Willis Music Co., Cincinnati, Ohio, used by permission.

The World of Peripole, Inc., for "Little Boy Song," reprinted from *Little Calypsos* by permission of the publisher, Carl Van Roy Publishing Co., Inc., Browns Mills, NJ, distributed by The World of Peripole, Inc., Browns Mills, NJ 08015.

Yahres Publications, Coraopolis, Pennsylvania, for "Hey, Mr. Echo," © 1961 by Yahres Publications.

Appreciation is expressed to Dr. Ralph G. Laycock, Brigham Young University, for his arrangements of songs found on the following pages: 4, 8, 9, 10, 15, 18, 22, 23, 24, 26, 30, 44, 50, 54, 55, 56, 58, 61, 62, 63, 65 ("The Old Gray Cat"), 66, 69, 71, 75, 76, 78, 79, 82, 86, 87, 90, 92, 94, 96, 98, 101, 107, 108, 114, 116, 118, 124, 125, 137, 139 ("Apple Tree Is Blooming"), 144, 146 ("Hear the Wind Blow"), 147, 148, 150, 152, 153 ("Halloween Is Coming"), 157, 160, 162, 163, 164, 165 ("Two Little Valentines"), 166, 168, 171, 172, 176, 179, 186.

The photographs of instruments in the introduction are by Russell J. Best, Brigham Young University, Educational Media Services.

ILLUSTRATORS

James Cummins, Jon Goodell, Mary Knowles, William Mathison, Lyle Miller, Carol Newsom, and Tom Newsom

CONTENTS

INTRODUCTION

"The poem gives expression to our heart, the song gives expression to our voice, and the dance gives expression to our movements. These three arts take their rise from the human soul, and then are given further expression by means of the musical instruments."[1] The blending of music, poetry, and movement has long lent joy to the human heart. Add to these the element of children, with their spontaneity, enthusiasm, and imagination, to create all that is necessary for many rich and delightful experiences.

Mockingbird Flight includes a variety of materials and ideas that will enable kindergarten teachers to share some of the joy and delight of music with their pupils. Let them sing the songs. Let them listen for moods, patterns, and phrases. Let them move freely and spontaneously. Let them play tonal and percussion instruments. Let them create accompaniments, words, movements, and tunes of their own. Let them grow in their musical understanding. Let them enjoy music and the richness it can bring to their lives.

SINGING

If children speak with any inflection in their voices at all, they can sing. Many kindergarten children, however, have never sung or have never learned how to sing. For a majority of these pupils, their attitudes about singing and about music in general will be shaped by you, their kindergarten teacher. It is difficult for children to separate comments about their voices from comments about themselves, because their voices are so much a part of their self-concept. Be encouraging and helpful. Avoid discouraging or embarrassing any child.

Teachers can help pupils sing well by singing often and by providing good models in themselves and in the records they play. Sing during special music time, sing when the children first come to school, and sing when they are going home. Sing when they are working in small groups or playing outside.

Play games with voices. Let pupils imitate very high sounds and very low sounds around them. Have them make their voices go up and down like a siren. Stop the siren on a high, sustained sound. Ask several pupils to *tell* you what they saw on their way to school. Then ask others to *sing* what they saw going home from school yesterday, so that the children can hear the difference between singing and talking.

Sing pupils' names when calling the roll. Have the children answer with their own tunes or imitate the ones you sing. Sing musical questions, such as, "What color is your shirt?" Ask a child to sing the answer. Be quick to praise and encourage when children are using good singing tone. Use simple melodic patterns in some of the songs as tone calls and help the children sing them alone or in small groups.

Encourage pupils to listen to melodies carefully and to reproduce them accurately. As children gain experience in singing, they will grow in their ability to sing songs with correct intonation. Help pupils sustain tones. Develop their ability to sing songs accurately by helping them breathe at regular intervals. Begin with songs that have short phrases; encourage pupils to sing whole phrases before they take another breath.

Finally, remember that little children have small voices. Encourage them to use their singing voices to their fullest potential, but never encourage them to begin yelling in order to sing loudly. Contrast singing *forte* and singing *piano* by making the *piano* as soft as possible and the *forte* their fullest singing voice.

---

[1]Lin Yutang, ed. and trans., *The Wisdom of Confucius,* The Modern Library (New York: Random House, 1938), p.261.

LISTENING

If children can become sensitive listeners, learning ability, not only in music, but in every phase of their lives, increases. Help pupils become aware of the sounds around them, in their classroom, on the playground, going to and from school, at home, downtown, and in a car or bus. Help them analyze these sounds as to pitch, duration, regularity, loudness, etc. Play guessing games with sounds that are in the room or on a tape recorder. Encourage children to use the sounds of things around them to create sound stories or informal compositions on tape.

Use recordings to help children listen for the way a song makes them feel. Ask questions such as these: How does it make you want to move? Which parts of the melody are high? Which parts of the melody are low? Which are loud? Which are soft? How many times do you hear this melodic pattern or that rhythmic pattern? Which phrases are alike? Which phrases are different? What instrument is playing? What kind of a voice is singing? Does the underlying beat move in twos or in threes?

Sing a tone pattern that the children can listen to and echo. Clap a rhythm pattern for them to imitate. Point out the difference between the I chord and the V_7 chord on the Autoharp. Ask how many times the I chord is played before it changes to the V_7 chord. Take the C major scale of the resonator bells out of the case and mix up the order of the bells. Give individual bells to eight children and have them put the bells in correct order by listening to the tones of each other's bells. Let pupils listen to several rhythm instruments and decide which ones sound like animals.

Lord Byron wrote in *Don Juan*: "There's music in the sighing of the reed; There's music in the gushing of the rill; There's music in all things, if men had ears." Help children listen for the music.

MOVING

Little children like to move. All different kinds of movements from finger plays to large muscle movements of the whole body should be included in a complete music program. Some of the songs in the book call for specific finger plays; others recommend that the children make up their own hand motions.

Some songs suggest an imitative type of movement, encouraging the children to move like a lion, a large ship, or a mouse. Others lend themselves to dramatization of a whole story or sequence of events. Still others may be adapted, through changes in meter and tempo, to basic locomotor movements such as walking, running, skipping, hopping, rolling, and sliding. Finally, many of the songs are singing games or simple dances with patterns to perform with certain parts of the music.

A listing of specific songs in each of these categories is found in the classified index. All kinds of movement are important. Each helps pupils develop a feeling for meter, tempo, even and uneven rhythm patterns, and interpretation of mood.

PLAYING INSTRUMENTS

There are many simple instruments which pupils can play to enrich their songs and movements. They fall into three categories: harmony instruments, melody instruments, and percussion or rhythm instruments.

HARMONY INSTRUMENTS

The Autoharp

The Autoharp is perhaps the most widely used harmony instrument in the elementary classroom. Children can play it most easily on one-chord songs because they can concentrate on keeping the rhythm and not on changing the chords. However, many pupils can learn to play two-chord and eventually three-chord songs as they learn to listen for chord changes in the songs they sing.

There is a physical problem that must be recognized. Many five-year-old children have hands and fingers that are too small or too weak to hold down the chord bars of the Autoharp. For this reason, it often works best for the teacher to do the chording and for the children to do the strumming. Help them feel the rhythm of the underlying beat by asking whether it is in twos or threes. Encourage them to accent the first beat of the measure as they strum. Let them strum strong-weak or strong-weak-weak, whichever is appropriate to the song.

Chord symbols are given with most of the songs in this book. Occasionally the melody is reprinted separately in a key more suitable for use with the Autoharp. The chord symbols are also helpful in using piano or guitar accompaniment.

MELODY INSTRUMENTS

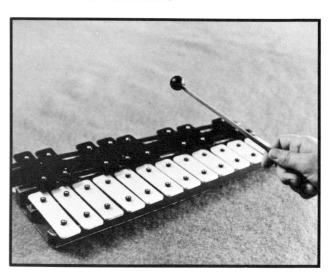

Song Bells

A set of song bells is a melody instrument, very portable and very handy. Refrain from referring to it as a xylophone. A xylophone is an instrument with bars made of wood, while the bars on the bells are made of metal and have a ringing quality that a xylophone does not have. Listen to "Fossils" from *Carnival of the Animals* to hear the sharp, penetrating sound of a xylophone.

The song bells are helpful in showing the up and down directions of a melody, especially when they are tipped up vertically on a table or other surface so that the higher tones are at the top and the lower tones are at the bottom. Children may use the song bells to accompany pentatonic songs on the black keys, play simple one-, two-, or three-note ostinatos, play a repeated melodic pattern in a song, or discover the relationship of the size of the bars to the highness and lowness of the tones. When having pupils play a melodic pattern or simple ostinato on the bells, it is helpful to mark the tones being played with a crayon or felt-tip pen that may be easily wiped off. As the children learn to read the letter names of the notes and play from charts using letter names, this is no longer necessary.

The piano keyboard may be used in basically the same ways as the song bells. The immediate advantage of relating size of note to pitch is not there, but this very fact may be the impetus for closer investigation of the inside of a piano by the class to discover whether the strings themselves vary in length or size in relation to the tones played. The piano is a natural medium for letting the children produce sound effects for songs, stories, and rhythmic movement.

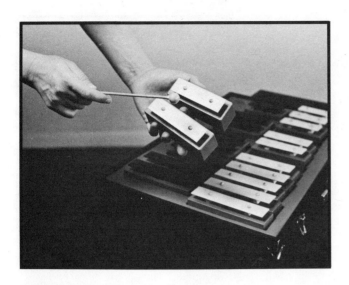

Resonator Bells

Resonator bells are similar to song bells. They are set up like a piano keyboard when they are in their case, and their size varies with their pitch. However, they have one distinct advantage over the song bells. Resonator bells may be removed individually from the case and played one, two, or three at a time. Therefore, it is easier for children to use them in playing melodic or ostinato patterns. Pupils may also arrange them in the order they will be played and thus do away with some confusion.

Encourage pupils to use any or all of these melody instruments to play introductions, accompaniments, and codas in the songs where they are specifically suggested and to create them when they are not. (See the classified index.)

PERCUSSION INSTRUMENTS

Any number of percussion or rhythm instruments may be used in the classroom. Each of them has a unique timbre, or tone quality. For this reason, most of them are a part of the percussion section of any large orchestra. They are real instruments, not just toys, and should be treated by the teacher and pupil with respect.

Teach the children to choose a particular instrument to enhance the mood of a song. A successful music program should include at least a half-dozen instruments, each with a different kind of sound. For example, a ringing instrument, a clicking instrument, a swishing instrument, a scraping instrument, a jingling instrument, and a drum would give the variety needed to show the kinds of sounds that may be produced. From these, the children can learn much about tone color and about selecting the right instrument for a special sound effect.

Give the children opportunity to explore each available instrument. Ask them to see how many different sounds it can produce. Let them discover how to play it: Can it be played fast or does it need time to ring? Ask them to play it louder or softer. Then choose an appropriate song with which to use the instrument. Ask several children to take turns playing it with the song.

In addition to adding sound effects and enhancing the mood of a song, percussion instruments can keep the underlying beat and the melodic rhythm of a song. They can also reinforce like and unlike phrases or sections and point out repeated rhythmic patterns. Finally, percussion instruments can add color that indicates the origin of a song. For example, add maracas and claves to a song from Mexico or the Caribbean; drums and wood blocks to a song from Africa; and temple blocks and finger cymbals to a song from the Orient.

The following instruments represent some of the more common ones that may be used. They are not all necessary, and some may be substituted for others called for in this book.

Rhythm Sticks

Rhythm sticks fall into the clicking category. They may be easily made from half-inch dowels, sanded and painted brightly. They are not too heavy, and two or three pairs would not be overpowering to most songs. Rhythm sticks are very precise and are good for playing a melodic rhythm or a particular rhythm pattern.

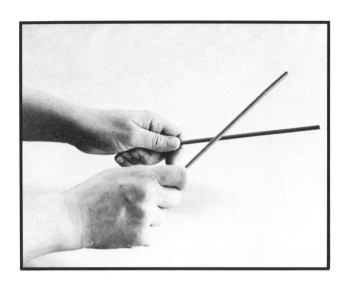

Chopsticks

Chopsticks are tiny rhythm sticks. They may be purchased commercially from import stores or made from the smallest dowels. They are very light and are excellent for the pitter-patter of rain or similar sounds. Chopsticks make a nice contrast in dynamics from the regular rhythm sticks.

The Guiro

The guiro is Latin American in origin. Its characteristic rhythm pattern in Latin America is long-short-short, long-short-short. The thumb and the index or middle finger hold the instrument in its large holes, and a narrow stick is used for a scraper. Its sound provides good contrast for the clicking instruments, and it may be used to represent the sound of a saw, a frog, a duck, a cricket, or any number of other things.

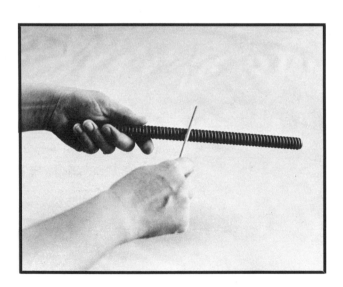

The Notched Rhythm Stick

The notched rhythm stick is sometimes sold with a regular rhythm stick. It may be used as a rhythm stick or as a scraping instrument similar to a guiro. It can be made from a three-quarter-inch dowel with a lathe. When scraped with a chopstick or a bell beater stick, it has many possibilities for sound effects and may be substituted for a guiro.

Maracas

Maracas are also Latin American in origin. They can be considered swishing instruments but are louder or harsher than the sand blocks. Maracas may be used as Indian shakers.

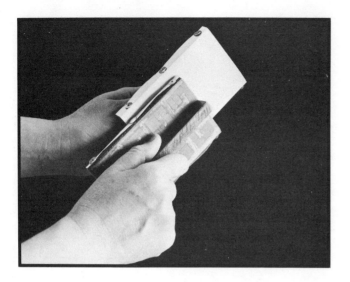

Sand Blocks

Sand blocks can be made easily. If two or three pairs are made, each with a different weight of sandpaper, you will have swishing instruments of varying dynamic possibilities.

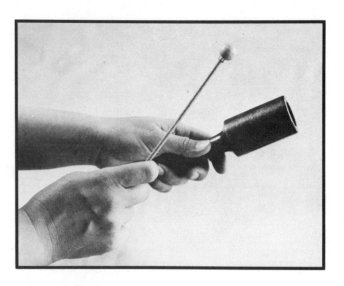

The Tone Block

The tone block is similar in sound but is not quite as loud as the wood block. It may be used wherever the wood block is called for. Two of varying sizes will also vary in pitch and can be effectively used for clocks ticking, horses walking or galloping, etc. They may be substituted for temple blocks or coconut shells. Some of them come notched and may also be used as a scraping instrument in place of a guiro.

The Wood Block

The wood block or the Chinese wood block, as it is sometimes known, is a very loud, sharp, clicking instrument. One wood block is usually sufficient in accompanying a song. It is very precise and is good for rhythm patterns and sound effects.

Temple Blocks

Chinese or Korean temple blocks usually come in sets of five, tuned to a pentatonic scale. They are hand-carved out of solid pieces of wood and have a very mellow clicking quality. They are expensive as a set but are sometimes sold separately. Two or three provide color for Oriental music and sound effects of walking, horses, clocks, etc. Coconut shells or the open ends of two paper drinking cups struck together may be substituted for temple blocks.

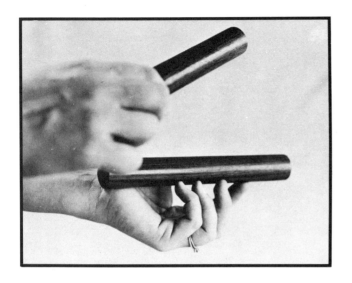

Claves

Claves are Latin American in origin. They look like fat sticks but are made of Honduras rosewood and are very resonant and very piercing if held properly. The clave being struck should be held as shown in order for the hand to provide a resonating chamber beneath the instrument. As a clicking instrument, it provides still a third dynamic level to the rhythm sticks and the chopsticks.

The Triangle

The triangle is a ringing instrument. It is best used in situations where it has time to ring. Usually children are urged not to touch the triangle itself, so that it may vibrate and ring. However, for a special sound effect such as the plumber in "Let's Build a House," it is better to grasp the metal of the instrument and then strike it. A triangle can easily be made from very large nails, which are suspended on a thin string and struck with a smaller nail.

Jingle Bells

Jingle bells, sleigh bells, or wrist bells are the only jingling instruments presented here. Individual bells may be purchased at many hobby or variety stores and secured onto a piece of heavy cloth, wide ribbon, elastic, or leather. They are most effective with four or five bells on each strap. Children may hold the straps in their hands or even put them on their wrists or ankles for Indian songs and dances.

Finger Cymbals

Finger cymbals, or antique cymbals, are ringing instruments which are lighter than the triangle. They may be struck together as shown for a light, ringing effect, or the faces may be struck together for a more percussive sound. Individual cymbals may be struck with a metal beater to give more children a chance to play them.

Bongo Drums

Bongo drums are paired drums of Latin American origin. They may be used wherever a drum is called for. The paired drumheads provide opportunities for great variety in rhythmic patterns.

The Tub Drum

The tub drum is a large, easy-to-hold drum which may be used wherever a drum is called for. However, if it is used in conjunction with bongo drums, it provides still a third, lower pitch for variety in drum patterns.

CREATING

Children should become involved in the creative process of music, not as a formal or a formidable process, but as a simple, spontaneous response to a given situation. If pupils are singing a song, they may want to add other verses telling about things they are doing or pets they have, or places they would like to go. See the listings in the classified index for songs which lend themselves to this activity. The pupils may want to put hand motions to a song where none are suggested or even add different ones where they are suggested. Children may want to move their whole bodies, imitating something in the song. They may want to dramatize the events of a song or improvise a dance to it.

As children become more familiar with the melody and percussion instruments, they may want to create their own accompaniments, introductions, and codas to many songs. For the pentatonic songs listed in the classified index of the book, the pupils may play as an accompaniment any note or combination of notes in the pentatonic scale used in that song. Pupils can use the piano to add sound effects to some songs or stories.

Finally, some children will want to create their own songs with original lyrics. Others may want to compose a song to go with a poem. The songs do not have to be long and involved, nor do they need to follow theoretical rules. The songs can be phrases pupils like to chant as they work or play. They do not even have to be written down. Various children may sing parts of a poem into a tape recorder. The important thing for any of these creative experiences is the act of creating and not musical perfection or preservation.

UNDERSTANDING MUSIC

There are many areas in which five-year-olds can grow and develop in their understanding of musical concepts. These understandings will come out of their experiences with music.

MELODY

Children can learn to identify octave jumps, high notes, low notes, scale patterns, and chord patterns in the melodies of songs by singing them, by playing them on the bells or on the keyboard, and by moving their hands and bodies up and down.

RHYTHM

Pupils can move their bodies appropriately, play percussion instruments, or strum the Autoharp to even and uneven rhythms, fast and slow tempos, underlying beats in twos or threes, and to the melodic rhythm of a song.

HARMONY

Through listening, children can learn to identify chord changes on the Autoharp and different kinds of accompaniments on song recordings.

FORM

By listening, playing instruments, moving, using dynamics, and contrasting the singing of small groups with the whole class, pupils can point out repeated rhythmic or melodic patterns in a song, identify verse-refrain (AB) songs, and underscore the sameness of like phrases or sections and the differences of unlike phrases or sections, thus identifying ABA form.

DYNAMICS

Children can learn to control their voices to sing loudly (not yell) or softly. They can learn to respond through singing and playing to terms like *forte* and *piano*. Pupils can also learn to get gradually louder (crescendo) and gradually softer (diminuendo) and identify these dynamic differences and changes in recorded music.

TONE COLOR

Through the exploration of the sounds around them and the use of percussion instruments, children can become very selective about which instruments to choose for particular sound effects. By listening to their own and other voices in the classroom and on recordings, pupils can identify men's, women's, and children's voices. They will begin to discriminate between some keyboard, orchestral, and folk instruments. Pupils will also be able to identify the sound of a solo instrument.

TEACHING SONGS TO CHILDREN

In teaching songs to children, keep in mind that they depend mostly on their ears and can learn things well by rote. The following are a few procedural hints that might be helpful:

1. Sing or play a record of a song several times before asking the children to sing it.

2. Ask the children specific questions before singing the song each time to give them something to listen carefully for. For example, say, "Listen while I sing the song and be ready to tell me how it made you feel." "What special person do the words tell about?" "What kind of sound is mentioned in the words?" "On what words does the melody go very high?" "How many times do you hear this rhythm pattern in the song?"

3. As the song is introduced and the children are listening, think of ways they can actively participate. Ask them to clap a special rhythm pattern, sing each time there is a repeated melodic pattern, raise their hands high where the melody goes very high, draw a picture in the air of the melodic contour of the song, or clap or tap the underlying beat of the melodic rhythm of a song.

4. When a song is very wordy, use pictures or flannel-board figures or let the children create hand motions to help them remember which words come when. It is often fun to put the pictures up in the wrong sequence and let the children listen carefully in order to arrange them in the proper order.

5. If the song is a long one, don't feel obligated to teach it all in one day. Let the pupils hear the whole song at least once so that they will know where the part they are learning fits in, but then concentrate on the refrain or some other repeated part the first day and learn the rest on subsequent days.

6. Vary your approach from day to day and from song to song. Try to find the most outstanding feature of the song as the focal point of the lesson. It may be some unusual words, a melodic pattern, a rhythmic pattern, repeated phrases, opportunities for dramatization or finger play, or a strong underlying beat. Use the song recordings, a small group of children who have previously learned the song, a guest in the classroom, or a tape recording made of someone else singing the song to vary the voice qualities with which the children become acquainted.

7. Above all, be enthusiastic. Help the children feel that the song is a very special one they will thoroughly enjoy singing.

Just You and Me

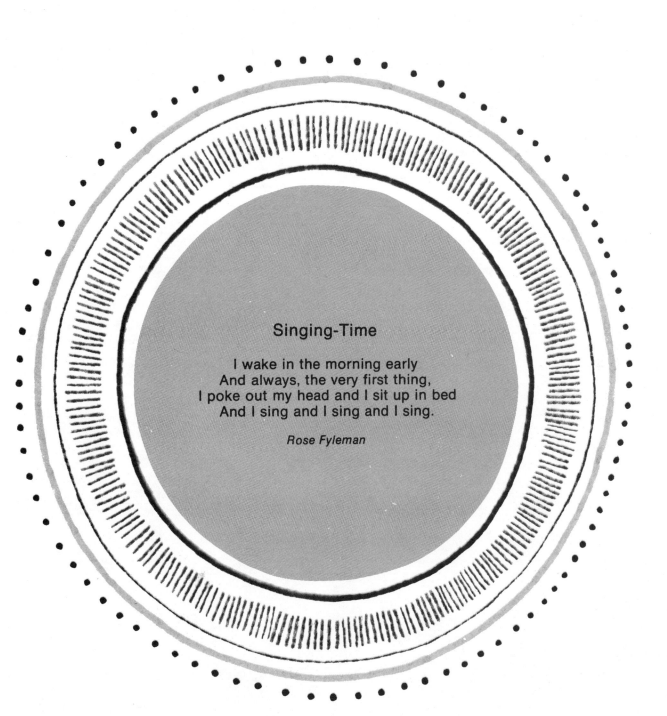

Singing-Time

I wake in the morning early
And always, the very first thing,
I poke out my head and I sit up in bed
And I sing and I sing and I sing.

Rose Fyleman

Who Are You?

German Folk Tune

Key: F major
Starting tone: C
Autoharp introduction: FF/C₇F
Beats per measure: 2/♩

Brightly Teacher

Good morn-ing to you, lit-tle boy, lit - tle boy, lit - tle boy, Good
girl, girl, girl,

morn-ing to you, lit-tle boy, who are you? I am John.
girl, (sing your name). Jane.

I am Ma - rie. I am Pe - ter. I am The-o-dore.
Je - rome. Ma - ry. Is - a - belle.

I am An - to - ni - o. I am Al - ex - an - der.
Do - min - i - ca. Ju - li - an - a.

Pupil: Good morning to you, Teacher dear, Teacher dear, Teacher dear,
Good morning to you, Teacher dear, who are you?

The names given in the song will assist you in helping children fit their names to the melodic answer.

Key: C major
Starting tone: G
Autoharp introduction: CC/G₇ C
Beats per measure: 4/♩

Good Night

Words by Lucy Mitchell
Music by Edna G. Buttolph

Good night, room, good night, light; Good night, win-dow; trees, good night.

Good night, stock-ings; good night, chair. Good night, peo-ple ev'-ry-where.

The children will enjoy making up hand motions to remind them of all the things they're saying good-night to.

Key: G♭ pentatonic
Starting tone: B♭
Autoharp introduction: Autoharp not used.
Beats per measure: 4/♩

After School

Chinese Folk Tune
Translation by Grace Boynton

Moderately   *Right hand plays 8va*

School is ____ out as the sun goes down; ____

Sustaining pedal throughout

Books in my bag, I go through the town. ____

Here are my par - ents, who smile at me; ____

I make a nice low bow like this, you see. ____

(♩) for repeat

This pentatonic melody may be easily accompanied by using any two, three, or four of the black notes in the high range of the piano or on bells. For example, try any of the following patterns an octave higher:

4

Key: F major
Starting tone: F
Autoharp introduction: FF/C₇ F
Beats per measure: 2/♩

Johnny's Jeans

Words by Louise Macbride
German Folk Tune

1. John - ny wears a   pair   of jeans, and   they   are   blue;
2. Jim - my has some   new——— shoes, and   they   are   brown;

Lin - da wears a   base - ball cap and   it   is   new.
Sal - ly has a   pur - ple coat to   wear   in   town.

Lis - ten how the   wind   blows, Lis - ten how the   roost - er crows,

John - ny wears a   pair   of jeans, and   they   are   blue.
Jim - my has some   new   shoes, and   they   are   brown.

The last two measures of the first, second, and fourth phrases constitute a melodic pattern
children can hear, play on resonator bells, and identify.

Adapted from *Growing with Music Book I Related Arts Edition* by Harry R. Wilson, Walter Ehret, Alice M. Knuth, Edward J. Hermann, Albert A. Renna © 1970
by Prentice-Hall, Inc., Englewood Cliffs, N.J. Reprinted by permission.

Key: C major
Starting tone: C
Autoharp introduction: CC/G₇C
Beats per measure: 4/♩

Let's Go Walking

Satis N. Coleman and Alice G. Thorn

Lightly

Let's go walk-ing, walk-ing, walk-ing, Let's go walk-ing,

far, far a-way; Let's walk back a-gain, back a-gain, back a-gain,

Let's walk home a-gain, back the same day.

Help the children create new verses to the song. Perhaps they will want to walk "over the hills" or "down to the store" instead of "far, far away." They may also want to change their mode of movement from walking to running, skipping, or hopping. Be sure to alter the tempo and underlying beat, if necessary, to accommodate the change in movement.

Running: same underlying beat, but much faster.
Tiptoeing: same underlying beat, but a little slower.
Hopping: same underlying beat, but staccato or detached.
Jumping: same underlying beat, but slower.
Skipping: change to 6/8 rhythm.
Galloping: a faster 6/8 rhythm.

Key: C major
Starting tone: G
Autoharp introduction: $CCG_7C/$
Beats per measure: 4/♩

Little Boy Song

This calypso song needs a few characteristic instruments for color. Try one or two or all of the following:

Tub Drum: Claves: Maracas:

Key: D major (C major)
Starting tone: B (A)
Autoharp introduction: (CCC/G₇G₇G₇/CCC) See below.
Beats per measure: 3/♩

Abi Yo Yo

African Lullaby

This African lullaby is supposed to be named for a monster who loves to frighten little children. The only way children can go to sleep is for their mothers to soothe the monster by singing his name over and over.

It would be appropriate to add some soft percussion instruments.   Sand blocks

Key: D major (C major)
Starting tone: D (C)
Autoharp introduction: (CCC/CCC) See below.
Beats per measure: 3/♩

Kum Ba Yah

Spiritual

mf 2. Someone's singing, Lord, Kum ba yah!
f 3. Someone's crying, Lord, Kum ba yah!
p 4. Someone's praying, Lord, Kum ba yah.
pp 5. Someone's sleeping, Lord, Kum ba yah.

The children will enjoy making up other verses.

9

Key: F major
Starting tone: C
Autoharp introduction: FF/C₇ F
Beats per measure: 4/♩

Today Is a Wonderful Day

Words and music by Charlotte G. Garman

mf To - day is a won-der-ful day,—— For I am go-ing a - way,——

Not to the cir-cus, not to the pool,—— Can't you guess I'm go-ing to school.

Tra la la la la, tra la la la,—— Tra la la la la, tra la la la.

Tra la la la la, tra la la la,—— Can't you guess I'm go-ing to school.

This happy song is a good one for helping children feel the underlying beat. Use a heavier percussion instrument (wood block, drum) on beats one and three and a lighter instrument (sticks, sand blocks) on beats one, two, three, and four.

Key: Eb major (F major)
Starting tone: Bb (C)
Autoharp introduction: (F/F/C₇/F) See below.
Beats per measure: 3/♩

Someday Very Soon

Words and music by Roberta McLaughlin

When I am old-er I'll fly to the moon, fly to the
I'll play my guitar, play my gui-
I'll sail in my boat, sail in my

moon, fly to the moon, When I am old-er I'll
tar, play my guitar, I'll
boat, sail in my boat, I'll

fly to the moon,
play my gui-tar, Some-day ver-y soon.
sail in my boat,

Help the children create and sing new verses about what they would like to do when they are older.

Key: C major
Starting tone: G
Autoharp introduction: CC/G_7C
Beats per measure: 4/♩

Hello, Ev'rybody

Words adapted from Eunice Holsaert
Music by Charity Bailey

Briskly

1. Hel - lo ev - 'ry - bod - y; yes, in - deed; yes, in - deed; yes, in - deed.
2. Good - bye ev - 'ry - bod - y; yes, in - deed; yes, in - deed; yes, in - deed. Stay

Let's make mu - sic; yes, in - deed; yes, in - deed, my dar - ling.
well and hap - py; yes, in - deed; yes, in - deed, my dar - ling.

Encourage the children to sing this song with enthusiasm. They need not sing it loudly, but with a little accent on each syllable, especially the "deed" of "indeed." Notice that the "in" part of "indeed" is sung shorter and the "deed" part is sung longer.

12

Key: F major
Starting tone: C
Autoharp introduction: FFFF/
Beats per measure: 4/♩

Beauty in the World

Words and music by Roberta McLaughlin

1. Be - cause I've walked in a cool, green for - est,
2. Be - cause I've sat by the rip - pling wa - ters,

Be - cause I've walked in a cool, green for - est,
Be - cause I've sat by the rip - pling wa - ters,

Be - cause I've walked in a cool, green for - est,
Be - cause I've sat by the rip - pling wa - ters,

I know there's peace and beau - ty in the world.

3. Because I've wandered in flow-'ring meadows, etc.

4. Because my brother gave me his hand, etc.

Clap the rhythm of the words as you sing the song to the children; then have them clap with you. Help them notice that the rhythm of the words is the same for the first three phrases.

Key: F major
Starting tone: F
Autoharp introduction: F/F/F/F
Beats per measure: 2/♩

Are You Sleeping?

French Folk Tune

Are   you   sleep - ing,   are   you   sleep - ing,

Broth - er   John,   Broth - er   John?

Morn-ing bells are   ring - ing,   morn-ing bells are   ring - ing,

Ding,   ding,   dong;   Ding,   ding,   dong.

Piano accompaniment: play either pattern throughout the song.

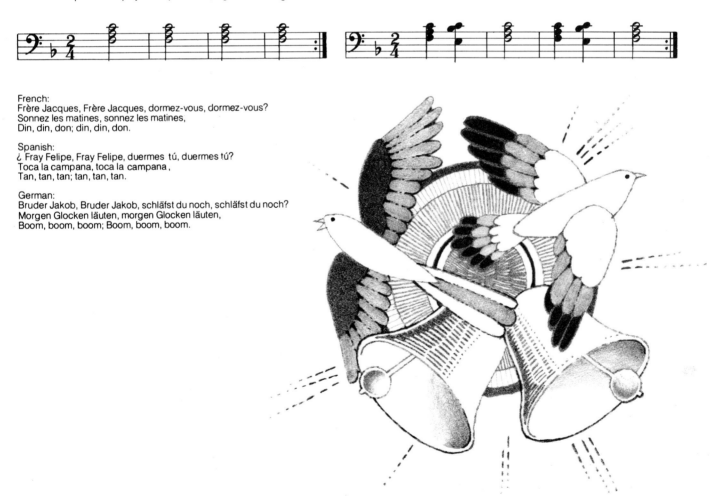

French:
Frère Jacques, Frère Jacques, dormez-vous, dormez-vous?
Sonnez les matines, sonnez les matines,
Din, din, don; din, din, don.

Spanish:
¿ Fray Felipe, Fray Felipe, duermes tú, duermes tú?
Toca la campana, toca la campana,
Tan, tan, tan; tan, tan, tan.

German:
Bruder Jakob, Bruder Jakob, schläfst du noch, schläfst du noch?
Morgen Glocken läuten, morgen Glocken läuten,
Boom, boom, boom; Boom, boom, boom.

Key: D major (C major)
Starting tone: F# (E)
Autoharp introduction: (CC/G$_7$C) See below.
Beats per measure: 2/♩

O My Little Boy

Folk Song from Alabama
Collected by Mae Erskine Irvine

O my lit - tle boy, _____ Who made your brit - ches? _____

O my lit - tle boy, _____ Who made your brit - ches? _____

O my lit - tle boy, _____ Who made your brit - ches? _____

Mom-my cut 'em out and Dad - dy sewed the stit - ches. _____

Other verses may be created by asking questions and having individual children supply the answers. For example:
    O my little girl, who makes your dinner?
    O my little girl, who makes your dinner?
    O my little girl, who makes your dinner?
    Mommy cooks the food, and Daddy sets the table.
The rhythm pattern at the end of each phrase is syncopated and may be emphasized on a wood block or other rhythm instrument.

Key: C major
Starting tone: C
Autoharp introduction: C DmG₇C /
Beats per measure: 4/♩

Smiles

Words by Daniel Taylor
Anonymous

Not too fast

1. If you chance to meet a frown, Do not let it stay,
2. No one likes a frown-ing face. Change it for a smile,

Quick-ly turn it up - side down, And smile that frown a - way.
Make the world a bet - ter place By smil-ing all the while.

Provide two pictures; one with a frowning face and one with a smiling face. These may be held back to back and flipped as called for in the song.

16

Jennie Jenkins

American Folk Song

1. Will you wear white, oh, my dear, oh, my dear?
2. Will you wear blue, oh, my dear, oh, my dear?

Oh, will you wear white, Jen-nie Jen - kins?
Oh, will you wear blue, Jen-nie Jen - kins?

I won't wear white for the col - or's too bright,
I won't wear blue for the col - or's too true,

I'll buy me a fol-de-rol-dy, til-dy-tol-dy, seek-a-dou-ble

roll, ——————— Jen-nie Jen-kins roll. ——————

3. Will you wear red?
   I won't wear red,
   It's the color of my head,
4. Will you wear purple?
   I won't wear purple,

5. Will you wear green?
   I won't wear green,
   For it's a shame to be seen,
6. Will you wear black?

   I won't wear black,
   It's the color of my back,
7. Oh, what will you wear?
   I've nothing to wear,
   So I'll just go bare,

Have the children make up nonsense verses about their favorite color or the color they are wearing. Play a game by having all children wearing the color named in a particular verse stand up.

From *Music Now and Long Ago, Music for Living Series* © 1956, 1962 Silver Burdett Company. Reprinted by permission.

Key: E minor (D minor)
Starting tone: E (D)
Autoharp introduction: (DmDm/A₇Dm) See below.
Beats per measure: 2/♩

All the Pretty Horses

American Folk Song

Right hand *8va*

Calmly Em   Am   Bm   Em

Hush - a - by, don't you cry, Go to sleep my lit - tle ba - by,

(8va) Em   Am   Bm   Em

When you wake, you shall have All the pret-ty lit - tle hor - ses.

(8va) Bm   Em   Bm   Em

Blacks and bays, dap-ples and grays, All the pret-ty lit - tle hor - ses.

(8va) Em   Am   Bm   Em

Hush - a - by, don't you cry, Go to sleep my lit - tle ba - by.

Ask the children to dramatize this lullaby by rocking a doll while singing very softly and smoothly.

Ask one child to play the descending scale passage at the end of each phrase on the resonator bells:

Key: C major
Starting tone: C
Autoharp introduction: CCC/CCC
Beats per measure: 3/♩

Mother Goose Lullaby

Words and music by Inez Schubert

Swaying rhythm

Coo - lee - i,   coo-lee - oo,   coo - lee - ee; _____

Close   your   eyes; what   do   you   see? _____   The

cat   on   his   fid - dle   is   play - ing   a   tune,   And the
fid - dlers   are   play - ing   for   Ole ____ King   Cole,   Who ____

old   cow ____ jumps   right ____ o - ver   the   moon.   Coo-lee -
laughs   as   he   shouts   for   his   pipe ____ and   bowl.

i,   coo-lee - oo,   coo - lee - ee; _____

Close   your   eyes; watch   them   with   me. _____

At Work and Play

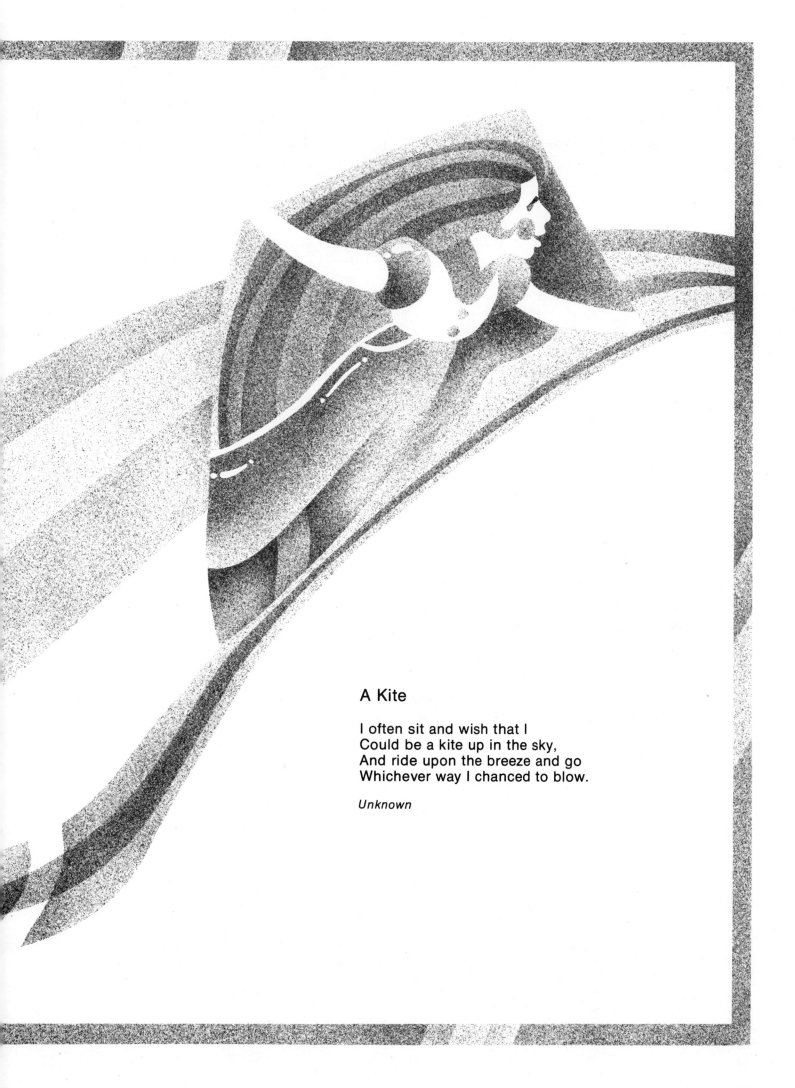

A Kite

I often sit and wish that I
Could be a kite up in the sky,
And ride upon the breeze and go
Whichever way I chanced to blow.

Unknown

The Little Shoemaker

Words by Alice C. D. Riley
Music by Jessie L. Gaynor

Key: F major
Starting tone: A
Autoharp introduction: FF/C₇F
Beats per measure: 4/♩

1. There's a lit-tle wee man in a lit-tle wee house Lives o-ver the way you see,——— And he sits by the win-dow and sews all day, Mak-ing shoes for you and me.———

2. He puts his nee-dle in and out, His thread flies to and fro.———With his ti-ny awl he bores a hole, Hear the ham-mer's bu-sy blow.———

Refrain

A rap-a-tap-tap, a rap-a-tap-tap, Hear the ham-mer's tit-tat-tee.——— A rap-a-tap-tap, a rap-a-tap-tap, Mak-ing shoes for you and me.———

Have the children act out the words of this song with their hands. They can make up hand motions for the "little wee man," the "little wee house," "lives over the way," and "you and me." Ask the children to make two fists and pound one on the other above their heads on the higher pattern and in front of them on the lower one. A wood block or tone block would also add to the effect on the "rap-a-tap-tap."

Key: F major
Starting tone: D
Autoharp introduction: FFF/FFF
Beats per measure: 3/♩

Good-Bye, Old Paint

Cowboy Song

Good - bye,—— Old Paint,—— I'm a - leav - ing Chey - enne.——

Good - bye,—— Old Paint,—— I'm a - leav - ing Chey - enne.

My foot in the stir - rup, my po - ny won't stand——

I'm leav - ing Chey - enne, and I'm off to Mon - tan'.

The form of this song is ABA, the last section being the same as the first. Accompany this song with coconut shells, paper cups hit together on the open ends, wood blocks, tone blocks, or a similar instrument. Emphasize the sameness of the A sections by using the same instruments on A and different ones on B or by using the same rhythm pattern on A (♩ | ♩ ♩ | ♩ ♩ |) and a different one on B (♩ | ♪♪♪ | ♪♪♪ |).

Key: F major
Starting tone: A
Autoharp introduction: FF/C₇F
Beats per measure: 2/♩

Sandy Land

From "American Play-Party Songs"
by B. A. Botkin

Make my liv-ing in San - dy Land, Make my liv-ing in San - dy Land,

Make my liv-ing in San - dy Land, La-dies fare-ye - well.——

The children may adapt the words of this song to any occupation they desire or to any specific part of an occupation:

Growing 'taters in Sandy Land . . .
Growing corn in Sandy Land . . .
Driving a truck in Sandy Land . . .
Teaching school in Sandy Land . . .

They may want to improvise an accompaniment on rhythm instruments that imitate some of the sounds involved in the occupations about which they are singing.

Key: G major
Starting tone: D
Autoharp introduction: G/G/D₇/G
Beats per measure: 2/♩

Let's Build a House

Words and music by Lucille Wood

1. Let's build a house,——— Let's build a
2. I'll be the car-pen-ter, I'll be the

Let's build a house,——— and work, work, work.
I'll be the car-pen-ter, and saw, saw, saw.

3. I'll be the plumber, I'll be the plumber,
   I'll be the plumber, and bang, bang, bang.
4. I'll be the roofer, I'll be the roofer,
   I'll be the roofer, and pound, pound, pound.

Sing as many verses as the children can think of about workers on a house, such as "I'll be the painter, swish, swish, swish." Let the children find sounds of rhythm instruments which would be similar to the sounds the workers would make:

    Carpenter might be a guiro.
    Plumber might be a triangle without a holder.
    Roofer might be a wood block.
    Painter might be a pair of sand blocks.

The last three notes of the song make a simple pattern to play on the bells:

The People in Your Neighborhood

Key: C major
Starting tone: G
Autoharp introduction: CC/G₇C
Beats per measure: 4/♩

Words and music by Jeffrey Moss

3. Oh, the grocer sells the things you eat,
   like bread and eggs and cheese and meat.
   No matter what you're looking for,
   you'll find it at the grocer's store.

4. Oh, who's the man who works each day
   to help to take the trash away?
   The garbage man's the man we mean,
   and he makes sure our streets are clean.

5. Oh, the doctor works the whole day long
   to keep you feeling well and strong.
   So if by chance you're feeling sick,
   the doctor makes you well real quick.

6. Oh, the bus driver will drive you anywhere
   when you get in and pay your fare.
   He will drive you fast or slow
   to take you where you want to go.

7. Oh, the baker is the one who makes
   your bread and rolls and pies and cakes.
   Come in and you will plainly see
   he bakes them in his bakery.

8. Oh, the barber has a great big chair.
   You sit in it, he cuts your hair.
   He snips and clips and just won't rest
   until he's made you look your best.

9. Now, if you've got an aching tooth,
   who'll make it well?   And that's the truth.
   The dentist cares for all your teeth,
   the top one and the ones beneath.

When additional verses are sung, use the first ending and return to the beginning refrain for each verse except the last to be sung, which is followed by the ending refrain.

Key: D minor
Starting tone: A
Autoharp introduction: Dm Dm/A₇ Dm
Beats per measure: 2/♩

Fire Song

Words and music by Roberta McLaughlin

Briskly

Hear the fire-bell,   hear the fire-bell,   Ding, ding, ding, ding,   ding,

Hear the si-ren,   hear the si-ren,   Ooo-ooo-ooo-ooo - ooo.

1. Shin-y en-gine,   hook and lad-der,   fire-men run-ning,   hear them shout.
2. Res-cue truck and   big red pump-er,   fire-men know what they're a-bout.

Pour on wa-ter,   pour on wa-ter,   put the fire _____ out!

The descending minor scale at the end of phrases one, two, and four may be played on the bells. The children may also "play" the pattern on their bodies by placing both hands first on their heads, then on shoulders, hips, knees, and toes as they sing.

Key: G major
Starting tone: G
Autoharp introduction: G/G/D₇/G
Beats per measure: 3/♩

If You Were a Farmer

Words by Louise B. Scott
Traditional melody

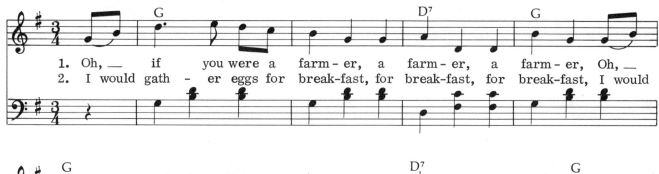

1. Oh, __ if you were a farm-er, a farm-er, a farm-er, Oh, __
2. I would gath - er eggs for break-fast, for break-fast, for break-fast, I would

if you were a farm - er, What would you do?
gath - er eggs for break - fast, That's what I'd do.

3. I would ride the cow to pasture.

4. I would milk the cow each morning.

5. I would feed the baby chickens.

6. I'd go plowing with a tractor.

Provide an opportunity for small group or solo singing by having one child or a small group of children sing the first verse. Have the other children sing the second verse in answer. The children who answer may perform appropriate actions as they sing. Follow a similar procedure with the remaining verses, alternating the first verse and an answering verse.

Key: G major
Starting tone: G
Autoharp introduction: GGGG/D₇D₇GG
Beats per measure: 4/♩

I've Been Workin' on the Railroad

Traditional

Key: G major
Starting tone: B
Autoharp introduction: GGG/GGG
Beats per measure: 3/♩

When We're Helping

Words adapted from Wallace F. Bennett
German Folk Song

Gaily

1. When we're help-ing we're hap-py, And we sing as we go;
2. When we're help-ing we're hap-py, And we sing as we go;
3. When we're help-ing we're hap-py, And we sing as we go;
4. Tra la la la la la la, Tra la la la la la;

And we like to help moth-er, For we all love her so.
And we like to help fa-ther, For we all love him so.
And we like to help teach-er, For we all love (him-her) so.
And we like to help oth-ers, Tra la la la la la.

Key: D major (C major)
Starting tone: A (G)
Autoharp introduction: (CC/G₇C) See below.
Beats per measure: 2/♩

What Shall We Do?

Game Song

Brightly

1. What shall we do when we all go out, All go out, all go out;
2. We will climb an ap-ple tree, ap-ple tree, ap-ple tree;

What shall we do when we all go out, When we all go out to play?
We will climb an ap-ple tree, When we all go out to play.

3. We will jump like jumping jacks, When we all go out to play.
4. We will play a game of tag,
5. We will ride our bikes around,
6. We will plant some flower seeds,
7. We will catch some lightning bugs,
8. We will go to the grocery store,
9. We will find some colored leaves,
10. We will make a big snowman,

Key: F major
Starting tone: F
Autoharp introduction: FFF/FFF
Beats per measure: 3/♩

Chiapanecas

Mexican Folk Song

Brightly

f Sing "Chia-pan - e - cas," Ay ay, Ay ay,

Sing "Chia-pan - e - cas," Ay ay, Ay ay,

Sing "Chia-pan - e - cas," Ay ay, Ay ay,

Sing "Chia -pan - e - cas," Ay ay, Ay ay!

Clap hands

The children will be able to hear like and unlike phrases in this four-phrase song. Phrases one and three are exactly alike. Phrases two and four are alike except for the last "Ay ay."

Have the children use drums, maracas, claves, and tambourines to accompany the song. One instrument may play the underlying beat of 1-2-3; another may strike just the accent or first beat of each measure; and still another may play the final "Ay ay" of each phrase.

Key: F major
Starting tone: F
Autoharp introduction: FFB♭B♭/FFFF
Beats per measure: 4/♩

Free to Be . . . You and Me

Words by Bruce Hart
Music by Stephen Lawrence

34

to a shin-ing sea In a land where the hors-es run free, And you and me

are free to be you and me.

Have the children form a circle and ask two or three of them to stand in the center. As the children sing the song, have those in the center walk in one direction and those in the circle walk in the opposite direction. At the words "Take my hand," have each child in the center take the hand of a child in the circle and lead the chosen child to the center. Continue until all the children have been chosen.

Key: C major
Starting tone: C
Autoharp introduction: CCG$_7$C/
Beats per measure: 4/♩.

The Merry-Go-Round

Words and music by George Mitchell

Gaily

Oh, how I like to go round and round   All day long on   a mer-ry-go-round.

1. Pranc-ing hors-es and kan—ga-roos,   Gai-ly gal-lop-ing two by twos.
2. Seals and ti-gers and ca-mels tall,   Oh, I wish I could ride them all.

Oh, how I like to go round and round   All day long on   a mer-ry-go-round

Suggested bell or piano accompaniment for first and last phrases:

Key: G major
Starting tone: D
Autoharp introduction: GG/D₇G
Beats per measure: 2/♩

Drum-de-dum

Words and music by Joan Gardner and Adelaide Halpern

The children could make up a drum part for this song, using a large drum or tapping rhythm sticks on the floor or on a chair.

From *Growing with Music Book 3 Related Arts Edition* by Harry R. Wilson, Walter Ehret, Alice M. Knuth, Edward J. Hermann, Albert A. Renna © 1970 by Prentice-Hall, Inc., Englewood Cliffs, N.J. Reprinted by permission.

Ping-Pong

Key: F major
Starting tone: C
Autoharp introduction: FF/CF
Beats per measure: 2/♩

Words and music by Mary E. Brougher

Ping - Pong. Play it with a pad - dle. Ping - Pong.
Ping - Pong. Play it with a pad - dle. Ping - Pong.

Play it with a ball. Ping - Pong. Play it on a ta - ble,
Play it with a ball. Ping - Pong. Play it on a ta - ble,

Play it night and morn - ing, An - y-time at all! Down = Up, Down = Up,
An - y - one can play it, An - y-one at all!

Send the ball a tum - bling. In = Out, In = Out, Chase it all a - round.

Win = Lose, Win = Lose, There's no use in grum - bling.

D.C. al fine

When you play it with a friend, You nev - er miss the time you spend on

A bell or piano ostinato may be played during the first eight measures of the song.

38

Key: D major
Starting tone: D
Autoharp introduction: DD/DD
Beats per measure: 2/♩.

Jump, Jump, Jump!

Words by Kate Greenaway
Music by Arthur C. Edwards

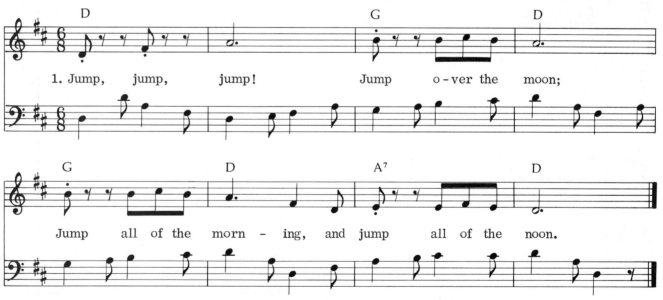

1. Jump, jump, jump! Jump o-ver the moon;

Jump all of the morn - ing, and jump all of the noon.

2. Jump, jump, jump!
   Jump over a star;
   Choose one that is twinkling,
   And not so very far.

3. Jump, jump, jump!
   Jump over the sea;
   Jump over the dry land,
   And jump over to me!

Have one group of children sing the first verse of the song while a second group jumps in time to the underlying beat of the song. Then have the second group sing the next verse while the first group jumps.

Key: C major
Starting tone: C
Autoharp introduction: C/C/G$_7$/C
Beats per measure: 3/♩

Let's Go Fly a Kite

Words and music by Richard M. Sherman and Robert B. Sherman

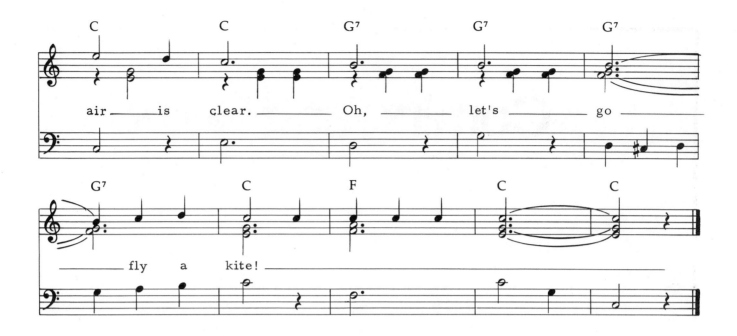

air _____ is clear. _____ Oh, _____ let's _____ go _____

_____ fly a kite! _____

Ask the children to make their voices get softer on the third phrase of the song and louder again on the fourth phrase.

Coming and Going

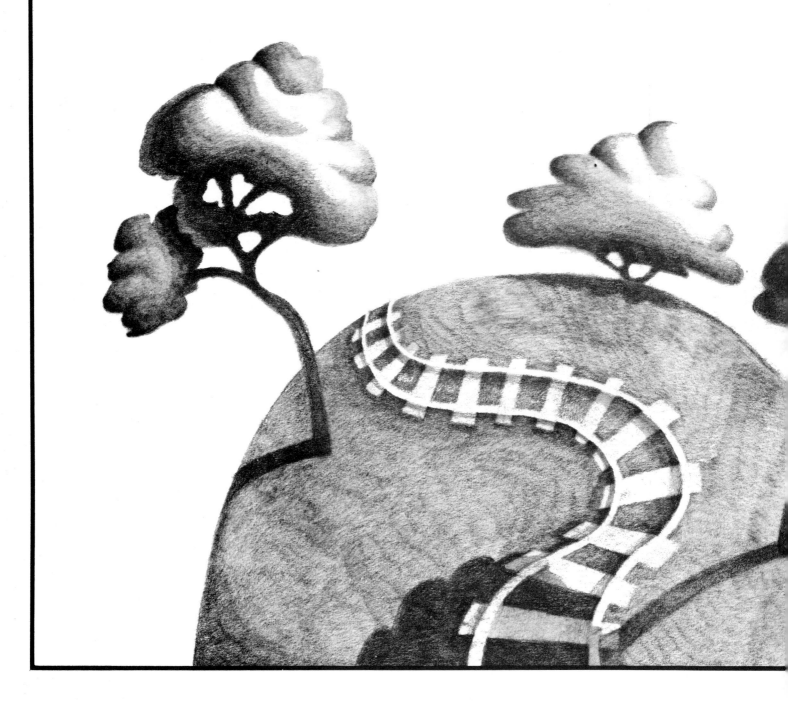

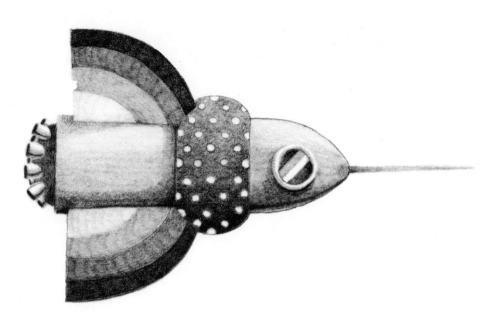

The Old and the New

Railroad tracks; the flight
of a rocket high above
in the starlit night.

Queenie B. Mills

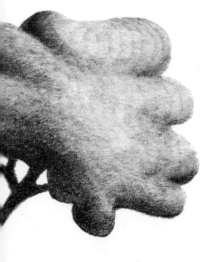

Key: G major
Starting tone: G
Autoharp introduction: GG/D₇G
Beats per measure: 2/♩

Goin' for a Ride

Words and music by Jeffrey Moss

Have the children select rhythm instruments or other sounds for the car, train, and boat. Ask them to clap twice or use the instruments for sound effects on each set of rests, since the pattern of rests is so regular in this song. In a meter of two beats per measure, this pattern emerges: "Oh, I'm goin' for a ride, (rest, rest) gonna sit behind the wheel. (rest, rest)," etc.

Key: D major (C major)
Starting tone: D(C)
Autoharp introduction: (CC/CC) See below.
Beats per measure: 2/♩.

The Railroad Train

Words and music by Charles Harvey

1. Click-et-y-clack, a - lunk, a - lunk! A train is com-ing a - chunck, a-chunck;
2. O -ver the bridge, a -cross the lake, A mile a min-ute it has to make;

A click-et-y-clack a mile a-way; It has-n't a sec-ond o' time to stay;
A ter - ri -ble snake with flam-ing eyes, That wig-gles and wrig-gles a-long the ties,

It sings a nois- y clack-et- y song, A rick-et-y, rock-et-y, rack- et-y song,
The cin-ders fall in fi - er- y rain, A tun-nel is wait-ing to swal-low the train

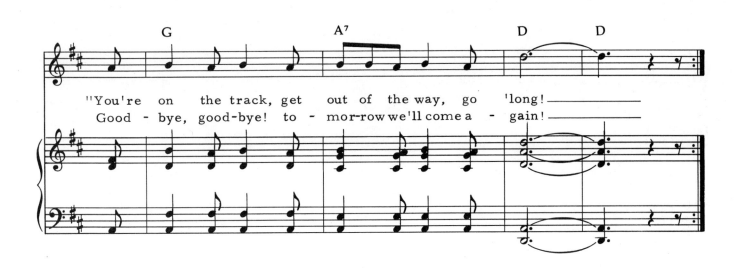

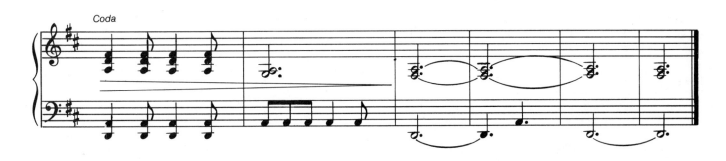

"You're on the track, get out of the way, go 'long! _____
Good - bye, good-bye! to - mor-row we'll come a - gain! _____

Coda

A few voices or rhythm instruments may be used as an introduction, accompaniment, and coda to this song. Add one instrument at a time, beginning with the slowest beat, during the introduction. Let all play together for the accompaniment. Then, drop one instrument at a time, beginning with the fastest beat, for the coda. Use the following as an example:

Guiro:

chug   chug

Sand blocks:
choo choo   choo choo

Sticks:
click-y clack-y   click-y clack-y

Key: G major
Starting tone: D
Autoharp introduction: GG/D₇G
Beats per measure: 4/♩

The Bus

Play Song

1. The peo-ple on the bus go up and down, Up and down,
2. The wheels on the bus go round and round, Round and round,

up and down. The peo-ple on the bus go
round and round. The wheels ___ on the bus go

up and down, ___ All through the town. ___
round and round, ___ All through the town. ___

3. The horn on the bus goes too, too, too, etc.
4. The money in the box goes ding, ding, ding, etc.
5. The wiper on the glass goes swish, swish, swish, etc.
6. The driver on the bus says, "Move on back," etc.

Have the children create movements with their bodies or hands to act out the verses of this song. Then ask them to choose rhythm instruments for sound effects:

Triangle or finger cymbals for the "ding, ding, ding"
Sand blocks for the "swish, swish, swish"

48

Key: G major
Starting tone: G
Autoharp introduction: GD₇/GG
Beats per measure: 4/♩

Now Let Me Fly

Negro Spiritual

Way down yon-der in the mid-dle of the field, See me work-ing at the char - iot wheel. Not so par-tic -'lar 'bout work-ing at the wheel, But I just want to see how the char - iot feels. Now let me fly, Now let me fly, Now let me fly way up high, Way in the mid-dle of the air.

The marked rhythm of this spiritual can be emphasized with a stamp-clap: stamp on beats one and three, and clap on beats two and four. The children can imitate things that fly — living things, toys, or machines — as they sing the refrain of this song.

From *Music Through the Day, Music for Living Series* © 1956, 1962 Silver Burdett Company. Reprinted by permission.

Key: F major
Starting tone: C
Autoharp introduction: FF/C₇F
Beats per measure: 4/♩

The Aeroplane

Not too fast

1. O the aer - o - plane, O the aer - o - plane
2. O the aer - o - plane, O the aer - o - plane,

Can go fast - er than the fast - est train;
How it flies so high I can't ex - plain;

Go fast - er than a ship at sea,
Just like a bird with sil - ver wings,

For it flies right thro' the air, you see,
And the mo - tor hums and hums and sings,

Up so high, Up so high, O I love to watch it fly.
Up so high, Up so high, O I love to watch it fly.

This is a good song to use to help children hear and identify the sound of an octave leap, or jump. Make a chart in picture notation of an airplane on the ground, then high in the sky. Have the children use their hands to show how the "aeroplane" goes "up so high." Ask them to play the pattern on resonator bells, song bells, or the piano.

Key: C major
Starting tone: C
Autoharp introduction: CC/G₇C
Beats per measure: 2/♩.

Taking Off

Words by Mary McB. Green
Music by Francis Hilliard

The air-plane tax-is down the field And heads in-to the breeze,

It lifts its wheels a-bove the ground, It skims a-bove the trees,

It ris-es high and high-er A-way up toward the sun,

It's just a speck a-gainst the sky And now it's gone!

Have the children act out the words to this song by using their bodies or model airplanes. Help them realize that as the plane rises higher and higher, so does the melody they are singing.

Key: D minor
Starting tone: D
Autoharp introduction: Dm Dm Dm / Dm Dm Dm
Beats per measure: 3/♩

My Rocket Ship

Words and music by June Norton

Ask the children to dramatize this song as they sing it by pretending to help an astronaut get ready to take off in a rocket ship. They may enjoy launching a toy or make-believe rocket after the countdown.

52

Key: C major
Starting tone: G
Autoharp introduction: CCC/CCC
Beats per measure: 3/♪

Whirlybird

Words by Margaret Fullerton
Old Tune

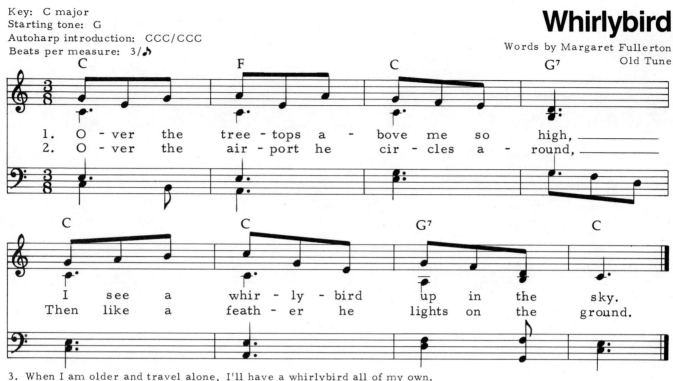

1. O - ver the tree - tops a - bove me so high, _____
2. O - ver the air - port he cir - cles a - round, _____

I see a whir - ly - bird up in the sky.
Then like a feath - er he lights on the ground.

3. When I am older and travel alone, I'll have a whirlybird all of my own.

Have the children move their arms in a circular motion over their heads, completing one circle for each measure in the song.

Key: G major
Starting tone: D
Autoharp introduction: GG/D₇G
Beats per measure: 2/♩.

Safety Song

Words by Margaret Lowrey
Flemish Folk Tune

Brightly

mf 1. We skip on our way to school each day, We
2. The green light says "Go," the red says "Stop"; A

nev - er like to be late; _____ When - ev - er we reach a
yel - low light in be - tween. _____ We look to the left and

traf - fic light, We know the sig - nal to wait. _____
to the right, And then we cross on the green. _____

Ask the children to dramatize this song. Someone can pretend to be the signal. The rest of the children can pretend to be walking or driving. As the "signal" displays the colors or directs the "walkers" and the "drivers" must obey.

Key: F major
Starting tone : A
Autoharp introduction: FF/C₇ F
Beats per measure: 2/♩.

Hey Diddle Diddle

From Mother Goose

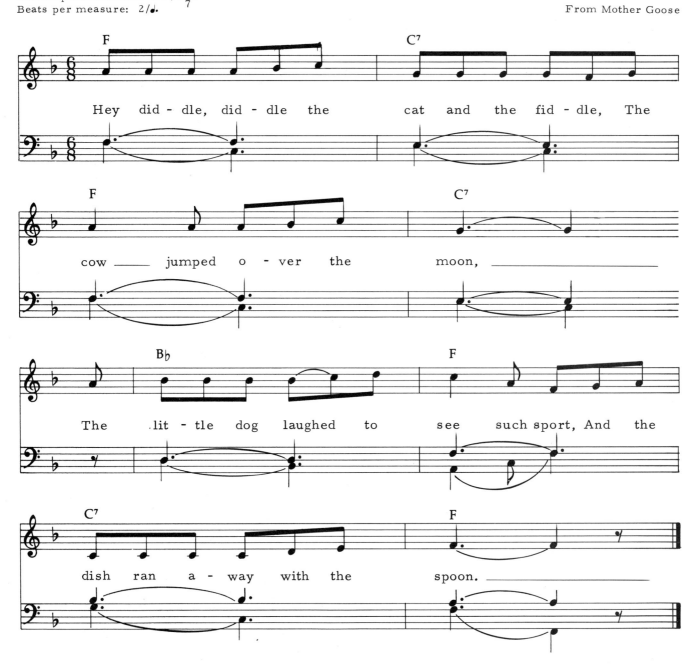

Hey did - dle, did - dle the cat and the fid - dle, The
cow ___ jumped o - ver the moon, _____
The lit - tle dog laughed to see such sport, And the
dish ran a - way with the spoon. _____

Briefly discuss with the children the ideas that make this a nonsense song. Let them use four different rhythm instruments for appropriate sound effects on each of the four phrases.

Key: D major (C major)
Starting tone: D (C)
Autoharp introduction: (CC/G$_7$C) See below.
Beats per measure: 2/♩

Twinkle, Twinkle, Little Star

Traditional

Have the children listen for like and unlike phrases in this simple ABA song. They may use finger cymbals or a triangle at the beginning of each measure for the A phrases and sand blocks on the underlying beat for the B phrase.

Key: G major.
Starting tone: D
Autoharp introduction: GG/D₇G
Beats per measure: 2/♩

She'll Be Comin' 'round the Mountain

American Folk Song

2. She'll be driving six white horses when she comes (whoa back).
   (last time: whoa back; toot, toot)
3. And we'll all go out to meet her when she comes (Hi, babe).
   (last time: Hi, babe; whoa back; toot, toot)
4. And we'll kill the old red rooster when she comes (chop, chop).
   (last time: chop, chop; Hi, babe; whoa back; toot, toot)
5. And we'll all have chicken and dumplings when she comes (yum, yum).
   (last time: yum, yum; chop, chop; Hi, babe; whoa back; toot, toot)

Ask the children to add appropriate actions to the words at the end of each phrase:
   toot, toot: Reach one hand up as if pulling on the cord of a train whistle.
   whoa back: Pull back hard on the reins.
   Hi, babe: Wave with one hand.
   chop, chop: Use one hand to chop at your neck.
   yum, yum: Use one hand to rub your stomach.

Key: F major
Starting tone: F
Autoharp introduction: FF/C₇F
Beats per measure: 2/♩

Little Red Wagon

Play-Party Game

1. Rid - ing up and down in the lit - tle red wag - on,
2. Hey! ____ what's happened to the lit - tle red wag - on?

Rid-ing up and down in the lit - tle red wag - on, Rid-ing up and down in the
Hey!____ what's happened to the lit - tle red wag - on? Hey! what's happened to the

lit - tle red wag - on, Won't you be my dar - ling?
lit - tle red wag - on? Won't you be my dar - ling?

3. One wheel's off and the axle's dragging. (three times)
   Won't you be my darling?
4. Hush your mouth and stop your bragging.
5. Or you'll fall out of the little red wagon.

Help the children make up original verses for this song:
   Riding to the store (the park, the zoo) in the little red wagon.
   Bouncing along in the little green car.
   Riding to school in the big yellow bus.

The descending scale pattern of the last two measures may be played on the bells:

Ask the children to "play" the pattern on their own bodies by using both hands to touch head, shoulders, waist, and knees once and toes twice each time they sing "Won't you be my darling?"

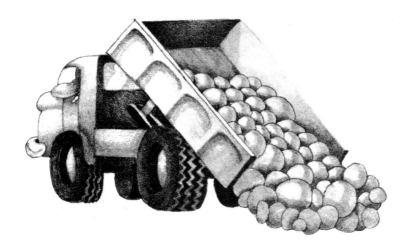

Key: F major
Starting tone: F
Autoharp introduction: FFF/FFF
Beats per measure: 3/♩

Did You Ever Drive a Dump Truck?

Words by Patricia Haglund Nielsen
Traditional Tune

Did you ev - er drive a dump truck, a dump truck, a dump truck?

Did you ev - er drive a dump truck and go through a town? __

Look this way, watch red lights, Look that way, watch green lights,

Did you ev - er drive a dump truck and go through a town?__

The words of this song can be adapted to the different kinds of trucks the children like (a tow truck, a pickup truck, a cement truck, etc.).

This song has a very strong rhythm grouped in threes. Use rhythm instruments or a stamp-clap-clap to help the children feel the meter.

58

Join In the Game

Ring-around-a-Rosy

Ring-around-a-rosy
A pocket full of posies;
One, two, three,
And we all fall down!

Mother Goose

Key: F major
Starting tone: F
Autoharp introduction: FF/FF
Beats per measure: 2/♩.

Johnny Works with One Hammer

Folk Song

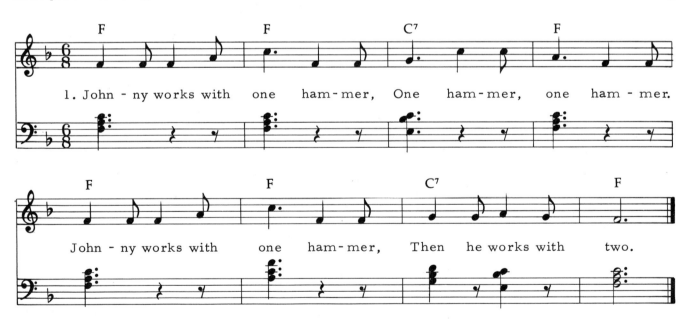

1. John - ny works with one ham - mer, One ham - mer, one ham - mer.

John - ny works with one ham - mer, Then he works with two.

2. Johnny works with two hammers,   Two hammers, two hammers,
   Johnny works with two hammers,   Then he works with three.
3. Johnny works with three hammers,   Three hammers, three hammers,
   Johnny works with three hammers,   Then he works with four.
4. Johnny works with four hammers,   Four hammers, four hammers,
   Johnny works with four hammers,   Then he works with five.
5. Johnny works with five hammers,   Five hammers, five hammers,
   Johnny works with five hammers,   Then he goes to sleep.

Key: F major
Starting tone: F
Autoharp introduction: FF/C₇F
Beats per measure: 2/♩

Head, Shoulders, Knees and Toes

Traditional

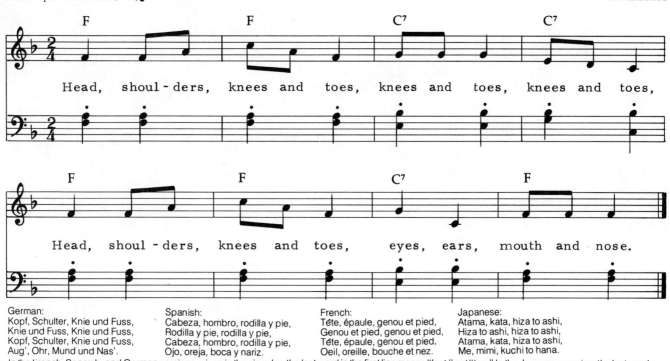

Head, shoul-ders, knees and toes, knees and toes, knees and toes,

Head, shoul-ders, knees and toes, eyes, ears, mouth and nose.

German:	Spanish:	French:	Japanese:
Kopf, Schulter, Knie und Fuss,	Cabeza, hombro, rodilla y pie,	Tête, épaule, genou et pied,	Atama, kata, hiza to ashi,
Knie und Fuss, Knie und Fuss,	Rodilla y pie, rodilla y pie,	Genou et pied, genou et pied,	Hiza to ashi, hiza to ashi,
Kopf, Schulter, Knie und Fuss,	Cabeza, hombro, rodilla y pie,	Tête, épaule, genou et pied,	Atama, kata, hiza to ashi,
Aug', Ohr, Mund und Nas'.	Ojo, oreja, boca y nariz.	Oeil, oreille, bouche et nez.	Me, mimi, kuchi to hana.

In the French, Spanish and German versions, given in the singular, the last word in the first line means "foot," not "toe." In the Japanese version, the last word in the first line means "leg."

Ask the children to stand while they sing and, with both hands, to touch their own body parts mentioned in the song. Speed up the tempo each time the song is sung. Encourage the children to find the words to the song in other languages. Have them teach the words to the class.

Key: D major (C major)
Starting tone: A (G)
Autoharp introduction: (CC/G₇C) See below.
Beats per measure: 4/♩

Follow the Leader

Words and music by Charlotte G. Garman

1. Fol-low the lea-der, Fol-low the lea-der, Fol-low the lea-der,

Do what I do.

2. Flop like a rag doll.
3. March like a soldier.
4. Hop like a bunny.
5. Sit down softly.

Ask one child to demonstrate a movement for the class to do while they sing the words. Then let the class follow the leader's actions while the piano interlude is played.

Key: F major
Starting tone: C
Autoharp introduction: FF/FF
Beats per measure: 2/♩.

The Farmer in the Dell

American Singing Game

The farm-er in the dell,——— The farm-er in the dell,———

Heigh - o the der - ry o, The farm-er in the dell.———

2. The farmer takes a wife, . . .
3. The wife takes the child, . . .
4. The child takes the nurse, . . .
5. The nurse takes the dog, . . .
6. The dog takes the cat, . . .
7. The cat takes the rat, . . .
8. The rat takes the cheese, . . .
9. The cheese stands alone, . . .

This circle game begins with one child in the center as the farmer. The children forming the circle walk or skip around the farmer while singing the first verse. An additional person is drawn into the center as indicated in each succeeding verse. At the end, all the children from the center join the full circle except the cheese, who usually becomes the farmer for the next game.

The C⁷ chord in the last phrase may be omitted, making this a good one-chord song for the Autoharp and an easy song for a child to play. A simple one-note accompaniment on the piano or bells may be improvised by repeating the note C in either an even or uneven pattern.

Key: G major
Starting tone: D
Autoharp introduction: GG/D₇G
Beats per measure: 4/♩

If You're Happy

Traditional

2. If you're happy and you know it, nod your head.
3. If you're happy and you know it, stamp your foot.
4. If you're happy and you know it, turn around.

Help the children make up additional verses to this song.

Key: C major
Starting tone: G
Autoharp introduction: C/G₇/C/C
Beats per measure: 3/♩

Come On and Join In to the Game

Cheerfully

1. Let ev - 'ry - one clap hands like me. (clap - clap)
2. Let ev - 'ry - one sneeze ——— like me. (ker - choo!)

Let ev - 'ry - one clap hands like me. (clap - clap)
Let ev - 'ry - one sneeze ——— like me. (ker - choo!)

Come on and join in to the game,
Come on and join in to the game,

You'll find that it's al - ways the same. (clap - clap)
You'll find that it's al - ways the same. (ker - choo!)

3. Let ev'ryone yawn like me.
4. Let ev'ryone jump like me.
5. Let ev'ryone sit down like me.
6. Let ev'ryone laugh like me.

This is a delightful singing game. The number of verses is limited only by the imagination of the children. Ask each child to take a turn leading the game with an original verse.

Key: F major
Starting tone: C
Autoharp introduction: FFC7F/
Beats per measure: 4/♩

Here Is the Beehive

Traditional

Slowly

Here is the bee-hive, where are the bees? Hid-den a-way where no-bod-y sees.
(Fist with thumb enclosed is hive.)

Watch and you'll see them come out of the hive,—— One, two, three, four, five.——
(Pretend to watch hive.)   *(Very slowly, beginning with thumb, fingers come out of the hive one by one, all fly away.)*

At the close of the song, the children will enjoy imitating the flight of the five bees by buzzing and waving their hands in the air.

Words from *The Rooster Crows* by Maude and Miska Petersham. Copyright 1945 by Macmillan Publishing Co., Inc., renewed 1973 by Miska F. Petersham.

Key: G major
Starting tone: D
Autoharp introduction: GG/D₇G
Beats per measure: 2/♩.

The Old Gray Cat

Traditional American Song

1. The old gray cat is sleep - ing,—— sleep - ing,—— sleep - ing,
2. The lit - tle mice are creep - ing, creep - ing, creep - ing,

The old gray cat is sleep - ing—— in —— the —— house.——
The lit - tle mice are creep - ing—— through — the —— house.——

3. The little mice are nibbling in the house.
4. The little mice are sleeping in the house.
5. The old gray cat comes creeping through the house.
6. The little mice all scamper through the house.

Ask the children to dramatize the words of this song. The dramatization can be underscored by changes in tempo and dynamics for each verse. For example, verse two can be sung very softly and a bit slower; verse five should be very slow and mysterious; verse six, of course, must move very quickly. The mouse that is caught may then become the cat for a repetition of the game.

Key: C major
Starting tone: G
Autoharp introduction: CC/G₇C
Beats per measure: Verse, 2/♩ Refrain, 2/♩.

Rig-a-Jig-Jig

Anonymous

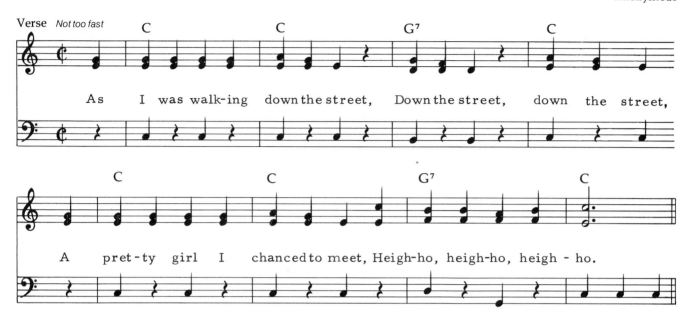

Ask the children to create new verses by changing the mode of going down the street and what it is that they meet. For example:

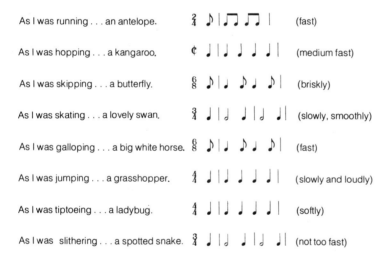

As I was running . . . an antelope.   (fast)

As I was hopping . . . a kangaroo.   (medium fast)

As I was skipping . . . a butterfly.   (briskly)

As I was skating . . . a lovely swan.   (slowly, smoothly)

As I was galloping . . . a big white horse.   (fast)

As I was jumping . . . a grasshopper.   (slowly and loudly)

As I was tiptoeing . . . a ladybug.   (softly)

As I was slithering . . . a spotted snake.   (not too fast)

Have the children skip each time they come to the refrain.

Refrain
Briskly

Rig-a-jig-jig and a - way we go, A - way we go, a - way we go,

Rig-a-jig-jig and a - way we go, Heigh - ho, heigh - ho, heigh - ho. ——

Marching Song

Key: C major
Starting tone: C
Autoharp introduction: CC/G₇C
Beats per measure: 4/♩

Adapted by Holsaert-Bailey
Negro Folk Melody

Oh, when we march——— and sing a song:———— Oh, when we

march and sing a song;————— Oh, don't you want to be in that

num-ber,——— When we march and sing a song?———

It is fun to experiment not only with changes in types of movement but also with changes in tempo and dynamics to complement types of movement. The song may be loud and brisk when the children are marching to the music, moderately loud and at an easier tempo as the children walk to the music, and very soft and slow as the children tiptoe to the music. Ask some children to accompany the march with claves or wood blocks, the walk with rhythm sticks, and the tiptoe with chopsticks or tapped pencils.

Where Is Thumbkin?

Key: F major
Starting tone: F
Autoharp introduction: FF/FF
Beats per measure: 4/♩

French Folk Song

1. Where is Thumb-kin, Where is Thumbkin? Here I am!—— Here I am!——

How are you this morn ing? Ver-y well, I thank you. Run a - way, run a - way!

2. Pointer 3. Middle Man 4. Ring Man 5. Little Man

Begin the game with both hands behind your back. Bring the appropriate finger or thumb on one hand around to the front at the first "Here I am!" and on the other hand at the second "Here I am!" Let them nod to each other on "How are you this morning?" and "Very well, I thank you." Then make the fingers or thumbs disappear one at a time behind your back on "Run away!"

Key: F major
Starting tone: F
Autoharp introduction: FFF / FFF
Beats per measure: 3/♩

Hands on Myself

Pennsylvania Dutch Folk Song

3. Nose-sniffer
4. Mouth-taster
5. Chin-chopper
6. Chest-protector
7. Bread-basket
8. Lap-sitter
9. Knee-bender
10. Foot-kicker

*On the first verse sing this measure twice with the same word. On the second and succeeding verses, sing the word for that verse first, then the word for each of the preceding verses in a cumulative manner.

This song may be sung as a leader-response type. The child who is the leader sings the first phrase and points to the appropriate body part; the class responds with the second phrase, indicating the same body part with their hands. Everyone sings the rest of the song together.

Key: D major (C major)
Starting tone: D (C)
Autoharp introduction: (CC/CC) See below.
Beats per measure: 2/♩

Rabbit in the Ditch

Words by Louise Macbride
Folk Song from Denmark

This circle game begins with one child in the center of the circle, curled up as the rabbit fast asleep. The children walk around the child and sing. When the words indicate, the rabbit's eyes open and the rabbit begins to hop. At the end of the song, the rabbit chooses another child to be the next rabbit by hopping to that child. Repeat the song as often as desired.

Looby Loo

Old English Singing Game

Here we dance Loo - by Loo, —— Here we dance Loo - by Light, ——

Here we dance Loo - by Loo, —— All on a Sat - ur - day night. ——

I put my right hand in, —— I put my right hand out, ——

I give my right hand a shake, shake, shake, and turn my-self a - bout. ——

2. Left hand
3. Right foot
4. Left foot
5. My head right in
6. My whole self in

This song is traditionally the story of the ritual of the Saturday night bath. To test the water, first one hand was put in, then the other, then each foot, and finally one's whole self. The "shake, shake, shake, and turn myself about" was probably to let the water cool.

Key: G major
Starting tone: G
Autoharp introduction: GG/D₇G
Beats per measure: 2/♩

Old Brass Wagon

American Singing Game

1. Cir-cle to the left, the old brass wag-on; Cir-cle to the left, the old brass wag-on;
2. Cir-cle to the right, the old brass wag-on; Cir-cle to the right, the old brass wag-on;

Cir-cle to the left, the old brass wag-on; You're the one my dar-ling.
Cir-cle to the right, the old brass wag-on; You're the one my dar-ling.

3. Everybody in, the old brass wagon.
4. Everybody out, the old brass wagon.

Help the children make up other verses:
    Skipping all around, the old brass wagon;
    Jumping in, the old brass wagon, etc.

Ask the children to perform the dance by forming a large circle and moving to the left for the first verse and to the right for the second verse. Have them walk slowly to the center, raising hands high for the third verse, and backward to the outside again, raising hands in back for the fourth verse. Make up appropriate movements to any additional verses.

Key: F major
Starting tone: C
Autoharp introduction: FF/C₇F
Beats per measure: 4/♩

My Hands

Words by Louise B. Scott
Music by Lucille Wood

Brightly

My hands up - on my head I'll place, Up - on my shoul-ders, on my face.

At my waist, and by my side, And then be -hind me they will hide.

Then I will raise them way up high, And let my fin - gers fly, fly, fly.

Then clap, clap, clap and one, two, three, Just see how qui - et they can be.

This song gives the teacher something constructive to do with hands that want to move. It also has three like phrases and a different one (AABA), which makes it a good song for helping children become more aware of form. The children may sing the A phrases sitting and the B phrase standing.

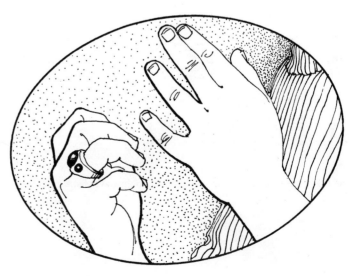

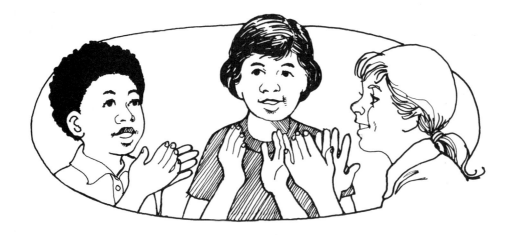

Key: C major
Starting tone: C
Autoharp introduction: C/C/G$_7$/C
Beats per measure: 2/♩

Clapping Game

Lila B. Pitts
Traditional (German)

All to-geth-er, here we go, Clap, clap, clap, clap, clap, clap!

Heads a-nod-ding, nod-ding so, Clap, clap, clap, clap, clap!

Slower *Faster*

All stand up and__ turn a-round, Clap, clap, clap, clap, clap, clap!

Slower *Faster*

Turn a-gain and__ then sit down, Clap, clap, clap, clap, clap!

As the children sing the song, have them perform the actions described.

Key: E♭ major
Starting tone: B♭
Autoharp introduction: (C major out of range)
Beats per measure: 2/♩

Dance with Me

Words from German by Patricia Haglund Nielsen
Music by Engelbert Humperdinck

Part-ner, come and dance with me, Both my hands I of-fer thee;

First go in, then go out, Then we cir-cle 'round a-bout.

1. With your foot— go tap, tap, tap, With your hands go clap, clap, clap,
2. With your fin-ger go tick, tick, tick, With your head go nick, nick, nick,

First go in, then go out, Then we cir-cle 'round a-bout.

Fine

Ask the children to form a circle for the dance. Have them join hands on "Both my hands I offer thee," then take two steps toward the center of the circle on "First go in" and two steps back on "then go out." Ask them to walk around the circle to the left on "Then we circle round about." The foot tapping and hand clapping are self-explanatory. For the second verse have them shake the index finger of one hand as if to scold on "With your finger go tick, tick, tick," and nod their heads on "With your head go nick, nick, nick."

Key: D major (C major)
Starting tone: A (G)
Autoharp introduction: (C/C/G₇/C) See below.
Beats per measure: 3/♩

My Hat It Has Three Corners

German Folk Song

German:

Mein Hut er hat drei Ecken,   Hut: hat
Drei Ecken hat mein Hut.   drei: three
Und hät' er nicht drei Ecken,   Ecken: corners
So wär's auch nicht mein Hut.

The first time this song is sung, the children sing all the words. The second time, the word *hat* is not sung. Instead, ask the children to make a motion as if to tip a hat. The third time, the words *hat* and *three* are not sung. The same motion is substituted for *hat* and three fingers are held up for the word *three*. The fourth time, the words *hat, three,* and *corners* are not sung. The same motions for *hat* and *three* are substituted. Ask the children to point to a bent elbow for the word *corners*. Begin the song with the whole class standing. Children who forget and sing a word they shouldn't, must sit down. Repeat the song, getting faster each time until only one child is left standing.

Key: F major
Starting tone: F
Autoharp introduction: FF/C$_7$F
Beats per measure: 2/♩.

Eency-weency Spider

Southern Folk Song

Een-cy, ween-cy spi-der went up the wa-ter spout;

Down came the rain and washed the spi-der out.

Out came the sun-shine and dried up all the rain,

And the een-cy, ween-cy spi-der crawled up the spout a-gain.

Key: G major
Starting tone: D
Autoharp introduction: GG/D₇G
Beats per measure: 2/♩

Little Cottage in the Wood

German Folk Tune

This song provides a good opportunity for children to sing "inside their heads." Ask the children to create hand motions for each two-measure section of the song. Sing it through once with the hand motions. Then sing the first two measures "inside your head" while doing the hand motions, and sing the remainder of the song aloud. The third time, sing the first four measures "inside your head" while doing the hand motions, and sing the remainder of the song aloud. Continue in the same fashion, each time singing two more measures "inside your head" until you are just doing hand motions and singing the entire song "inside your head." Help the children perform the song in the same way.

Key: C major
Starting tone: E
Autoharp introduction: CCCC/
Beats per measure: 4/♩

Elephant Song

South American Folk Song

Ponderously

1. One el - e - phant went out to play, _____
Out on a spi - der's _____ web one day.
He had such e - nor - mous fun, _____
He called for an - oth - er el - e - phant to come. _____

2. Two elephants went out to play,
Out on a spider's web one day.
They had such enormous fun,
They called for another elephant to come.

One child begins the game by imitating an elephant while the class sings the first verse slowly and heavily. Then the child chooses another "elephant" to join in as the class sings the second verse. The last elephant chosen then chooses a new one to make three. Continue this singing game until several of the children are imitating elephants.

79

Fly with Me

Bees

Every bee

that

ever was

was

partly

sting

and partly

. . . buzz.

Jack Prelutsky

Key: G major
Starting tone: D
Autoharp introduction: GG/D$_7$G
Beats per measure: 4/♩

Five Little Butterflies

Traditional

Verse *Gaily*

G   C

1. Five lit - tle but - ter - flies   Rest - ing at the door;
2. Four lit - tle but - ter - flies   Sit - ting in a tree;

sim.

D^7 G

One flew a - way And   then there were four.
One flew a - way And   then there were three.

Refrain   G   D^7

But - ter - fly, but - ter - fly,   hap - py and gay;

D^7 G

But - ter - fly, but - ter - fly,   fly a - way.

3. Three little butterflies Looking at you,
   One flew away And then there were two.
4. Two little butterflies Sitting in the sun,
   One flew away And then there was one.
5. One little butterfly Left all alone,
   He flew away And then there was none.

Have individual children or small groups sing the verse of this song and ask the rest of the class to join in on the refrain. Choose five children to be butterflies and let them dramatize the song while the rest of the class sings.

82

Key: D major (C major)
Starting tone: F♯ (E)
Autoharp introduction: (CCCC) See below.
Beats per measure: 4/♩

Three Blue Pigeons

American Folk Song

1. Three blue pi-geons sit-ting on the wall.
2. Two blue pi-geons sit-ting on the wall.

Three blue pi - geons sit-ting on the wall. (Words in italics are to be
Two blue pi - geons sit-ting on the wall. spoken after verse.)

1. *One flew away.*
   O-o-oh!

2. *Another flew away.*
   O-o-o-o-oh!

3. One blue pigeon sitting on the wall.
   One blue pigeon sitting on the wall.
   And the third flew away! O-o-o-o-o-oh!

4. No blue pigeons sitting on the wall.
   No blue pigeons sitting on the wall.
   One flew back. Whee-ee-ee!

5. One blue pigeon sitting on the wall.
   One blue pigeon sitting on the wall.
   Another flew back. Whee-ee-ee-ee!

6. Two blue pigeons sitting on the wall.
   Two blue pigeons sitting on the wall.
   And the third flew back! Whee-ee-ee-ee-ee-ee!

7. Three blue pigeons sitting on the wall.
   Three blue pigeons sitting on the wall.
   (Jubilantly)

Help the children dramatize this song. Change the color of the pigeons to give children who are wearing different colored clothes the opportunity to be pigeons. Encourage the children to underscore the sad mood of verse four by singing it slowly and sadly.

From *Music Through the Day, Music for Living Series* © 1956, 1962 Silver Burdett Company. Reprinted by permission.

In the Apple Tree

Key: G major
Starting tone: D
Autoharp introduction: GD₇/GG
Beats per measure: 4/♩

Words adapted
American Folk Melody

1. Can you hear how the rob - in sings in the ap - ple tree?
2. Do you know why she's sing - ing there in the ap - ple tree?

Hear her song; she is hap - py as can be.
In her nest there are blue eggs, one, two, three.

Ask the children to play this melody pattern on resonator bells, song bells, or the piano.
Display the pattern in picture notation. The children may "read" the notation and identify it each time it occurs in the song.

Key: G major
Starting tone: D
Autoharp introduction: GGG/GGG
Beats per measure: 3/♩

The Mexican Woodpecker

Words and music by Ralph Martucci

A Mex-i-can wood-peck-er high in a tree, Went chick-chick-a chick-a chick all the day, *(clap - clap)*
He got so am - bi - tious he wore off his beak, Now you can hear him say, ___

"Oh my beak, *(clap-clap - clap)* Oh, my beak, *(clap-clap - clap)* What a sad day when I lost it! ___
Hear me cry, *(clap-clap - clap)* Hear me sigh, *(clap-clap - clap)* What a sor - ry sight to see, Poor me!"

Emphasize the places where voices rest in this song by clapping (as indicated in the music) or by playing wood blocks, claves, or sticks. Other Mexican instruments such as maracas, drums, or tambourines could be used to accent the first beat of each measure. Provide an opportunity for small-group or solo singing by letting one child or a small group of children sing the woodpecker's lines (the last half of the song) and the whole class sing the story part of the song (the first half).

Key: G major
Starting tone: B
Autoharp introduction: GGG/GGG
Beats per measure: 3/♩

Kuckuck (The Cuckoo Bird)

English version by Katherine Rohrbough
Folk Song from Austria

Verse *Happily*

Oh, I went to— Pe-ter's flow-ing spring Where the wa-ter's so good:
German: Und jetzt gäng i an Pe-ters Brun-ne-le, Und da trink i so fein,

And I heard there the cuc-koo, As she called from the wood.
Und da hör' i den Kuc-kuck, Aus der Moos-bu-de schrei'n.

G   Am   D⁷
A   A   A

Ho - li - ah.

Refrain

Ho - le-rah ki -ki-ah   Ho - le-rah kuc-kuck,   Ho-le-rah ki-ki-ah   Ho - le-rah kuc-kuck.

Ho - le-rah ki - ki - ah   Ho - le-rah kuc-kuck,   Ho - le-rah ki - ki - ah   ho!

The following hand motions may be added to "Kuckuck." The letter A and the numbers correspond to the beats of the music as marked.

A. Pat hands on knees.

1. Slap knees.	2. Clap hands.	3. Slap knees.
1. Clap hands.	2. Snap fingers.	3. Clap hands.
1. Slap knees.	2. Cross arms and slap knees.	3. Uncross arms and slap knees.

Repeat each 1-2-3 pattern as many times as necessary to finish the refrain. The children may make up additional patterns after working with these.

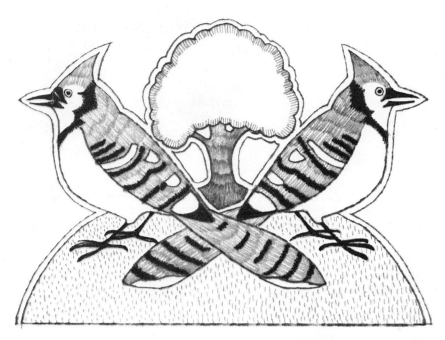

Key: D major (C major)
Starting tone: D (C)
Autoharp introduction: (CC/G₇C) See below.
Beats per measure: 2/♩

Two Little Blue Jays

Traditional tune

Two lit-tle blue jays sit-ting on a hill,   One named Jack and one named Jill.

Fly a-way Jack,   Fly a-way Jill,   Come a-gain Jack,   Come a-gain Jill,

Two lit-tle blue jays   sit-ting on a hill,   One named Jack and   one named Jill.

Have the children make finger puppets of two little birds, one for each index finger. Explain to the children that the finger play begins with the puppets in front of them. When the words to the song indicate, they make the "birds" fly away behind their backs, one at a time, and then return, one at a time.

Key: D major (C major)
Starting tone: D (C)
Autoharp introduction: (CC/G₇C) See below.
Beats per measure: 2/♩

Little Redbird in the Tree

American Folk Song—Georgia Version

1. Lit-tle red-bird in the tree, in the tree, in the tree, Lit-tle red-bird
2. Lit-tle snow-bird in the tree, in the tree, in the tree, Lit-tle snow-bird

in the tree, sing a song to me. Sing a-bout the ros - es
in the tree, sing a song to me. Sing a-bout the cloud-land

On the gar-den wall. Sing a-bout the bird swings In the tree-top tall.
Way up in the sky. When you go there call - ing, Do your bird-ies cry?

3. Little bluebird in the tree, In the tree, in the tree,
   Little bluebird in the tree, Sing a song to me.
   Sing about the mountains, Lovely they must be.
   Sing about the steamboats Out there on the sea.
4. Little blackbird in the tree, etc.
   Sing about the farmer Planting peas and beans.
   Sing about the harvest, I know what that means.

Help the children identify the form of this song as ABA. Ask them to emphasize the sameness of the A sections at the beginning and at the end by playing the same rhythm instrument on A and a different one on B, by having the whole class sing A and a small group sing B, by singing A loudly and B softly, or by creating special movements for A and others for B.

From Music for Early Childhood, New Music Horizons Series © 1952 Silver Burdett Company. Reprinted by permission.

Key: D major (C major)
Starting tone: D (C)
Autoharp introduction: (CC/G₇C) See below.
Beats per measure: 4/♩

All the Birds

Words by Alice Snyder Knuth
German Folk Melody

All the birds re - turn in the spring, Lis - ten to their sing - ing;

Rob- in, black-bird, lark and wren, Whis-tling, pip- ing, home a - gain,

All the birds re - turn in the spring, Lis - ten to their sing - ing.

The form of this song is similar to that of "Little Redbird in the Tree" except that A is sung twice at the beginning, making the form AABA. Use similar activities to emphasize the sameness of A. The melodic pattern of the first measure is a broken chord. Have the children play it on resonator bells or song bells whenever it occurs.

If you are using an Autoharp in "C," play:

Key: F major
Starting tone: F
Autoharp introduction: FF/C₇F
Beats per measure: 4/♩

Alouette

French-Canadian Folk Song

3. Le nez
4. Le dos
5. Les pattes
6. Le cou

*Repeat this measure to include the words for each preceding verse. For example, in the third verse, sing "Et le nez, et le nez, Et le bec, et le bec, Et la tête, et la tête," then continue.

"Gentil' Alouette" is a "pretty meadow lark."
"Je te plumerai" means "I shall pluck off your feathers."
"La tête" means "head."
"Le bec" means "beak."
"Le nez" means "nose."
"Le dos" means, "back."
"Les pattes" means "feet."
"Le cou" means "neck."

Have individual children take turns singing the solo parts on each verse.

Ask the children to choose rhythm instruments to play for each body part named in the song. Have a child play the instrument each time that part of the body is mentioned.

Over in the Meadow

The Purple Cow

I never saw a Purple Cow,
    I never hope to see one;
But I can tell you, anyhow,
    I'd rather see than be one.

Gelett Burgess

Key: D major (C major)
Starting tone: A (G)
Autoharp introduction: (CC/CC) See below.
Beats per measure: 2/♩

Over in the Meadow

Traditional English Nursery Song

1. O - ver in the mea - dow in the sand, in the sun,

Lived an old moth - er toad - ie and her lit - tle toad - ie one.

"Hop!" said the moth - er. "I hop," said the one.

So they hopped and were glad in the sand, in the sun.

Ask the children to use their fingers for the counting part of this song. Let them create an appropriate action with their hands or their whole bodies for the movement each creature makes. Flannel-board pictures and numbers add to the presentation of this song.

2. Over in the meadow, where the stream runs blue,
   Lived an old mother fishy and her little fishies two.
   "Swim," said the mother; "We swim," said the two,
   So they swam and were glad where the stream runs blue.

4. Over in the meadow, by an old barn door,
   Lived an old mother rat and her little ratties four,
   "Gnaw," said the mother; "We gnaw," said the four,
   So they gnawed and were glad by the old barn door.

6. Over in the meadow, in a nest built of sticks,
   Lived an old mother crow and her little crows six.
   "Caw," said the mother; "We caw," said the six,
   So they cawed and were glad in a nest built of sticks.

8. Over in the meadow, on a log by the gate,
   Lived an old mother lizard and her little lizards eight.
   "Crawl," said the mother; "We crawl," said the eight,
   So they crawled and were glad on a log by the gate.

10. Over in the meadow, in a big old den,
    Lived an old mother rabbit, and her little rabbits ten.
    "Jump," said the mother; "We jump," said the ten,
    So they jumped and were glad in a big old den.

3. Over in the meadow, in a nest in a tree,
   Lived an old mother birdie and her little birdies three.
   "Sing," said the mother; "We sing," said the three,
   So they sang and were glad in a nest in a tree.

5. Over in the meadow, in a snug beehive,
   Lived an old mother bee and her little bees five.
   "Buzz," said the mother; "We buzz," said the five.
   So they buzzed and were glad in a snug beehive.

7. Over in the meadow, where the grass grows even.
   Lived an old mother mouse and her little mousies seven.
   "Run," said the mother; "We run," said the seven,
   So they ran and were glad where the grass grows even.

9. Over in the meadow, by a pond in a line,
   Lived an old mother duck and her little duckies nine.
   "Swim," said the mother; "We swim," said the nine,
   So they swam and were glad by a pond in a line.

Key: F major
Starting tone: C
Autoharp introduction: FF/C₇F
Beats per measure: 2/♩.

A Little Gray Squirrel

Words and music by Charlotte G. Garman

Happily

A lit-tle gray squir-rel lives up in my tree, He chat-ters and chat-ters and chat-ters at me. He runs and he jumps in a bus-y way, gath-er-ing nuts for a win-ter's day. Bush-y-tail, Bush-y-tail, up in my tree, I like you, I like you, as you can see, Bush-y-tail, Bush-y-tail, up in my tree, Won't you come down — to play with me?

The three-tone descending scale pattern found in the verse of this song appears four times on three different pitches. Ask the children to listen for it and to try playing it on the bells. Then ask them the following questions:
Which time is it the highest?
Which time is it the lowest?
Which one is heard more than once?

Key: D major (C major)
Starting tone: D (C)
Autoharp introduction: (CC/CC) See below.
Beats per measure: 2/♩

The Fox and the Goose

German Folk Song

Fox, you stole our goose last night, You picked the fat-test one.
Fuchs, du hast die Gans ge - stoh - len, Gib sie wie - der her,

Picked the fat - test one,
Gib sie wie - der her,

Now the hunt - er's gone to get you With his horse and gun-gun-gun,
Sonst wird dich der Jä - ger ho - len Mit dem Schiess - ge - wehr,

Now the hunt - er's gone to get you With his horse and gun.
Sonst wird dich der Jä - ger ho - len Mit dem Schiess - ge - wehr.

Good examples of a scale pattern and a chord pattern appear in this song. Have the children "play" the patterns on their bodies, using feet, knees, waist, shoulders, and head for the first five steps of the scale, or on bells.

If you are using an Autoharp in C, play:

Key: G major
Starting tone: G
Autoharp introduction: GG/D$_7$G
Beats per measure: 4/♩

Old MacDonald

Traditional

Happily

Old Mac-Don-ald had a farm, E - I - E - I - O!

And on this farm he had some chicks, E - I - E - I - O!

With a chick chick here and a chick chick there,

Here a chick, there a chick, Ev'-ry-where a chick chick,

Old Mac-Don-ald had a farm, E - I - E - I - O

Add verses about any farm animals the children may know, such as ducks, turkeys, sheep, cows, and pigs. Have the children make and use sack puppets for each animal. Ask the children to choose rhythm instruments for sound effects on each verse. Make the song a cumulative one by repeating the part between the signs (+) for as many animals as have been introduced.

This song may be played on the black keys of the piano by moving all the tones down one-half step. Any of the black keys may then be used as a simple accompaniment. For example:

Keep repeating the pattern throughout the song.

Key: F major
Starting tone: A
Autoharp introduction: FF/C₇F
Beats per measure: 4/♩

Tinga Layo

Calypso Song from the West Indies

The melody pattern of the words "Tinga Layo" is easy to sing and is often repeated. It could be played on the bells or used as a solo while the rest of the class sings the remainder of the song. Calypso instruments enhance the flavor of this song. Have the children use instruments to play the rhythm patterns of some of the words.

Bongo, conga, or tub drum: Lay - O   Maracas: Come lit-tle don-key, Come lit-tle don-key   Claves: My don-key, walk, My don-key, talk

Key: F major
Starting tone: F
Autoharp introduction: FF/C₇F
Beats per measure: 2/♩

My Farm (Mi Chacra)

Translation by Olcutt and Phyllis Sanders
Folk Song from Argentina

Verse *Brightly*

1. Come, come and see my farm, for it is love - ly.
Spanish: Ven - gan a ver mi cha - cra que es her - mo - sa.

Come, come and see my farm, for it is love - ly.
Ven - gan a ver mi cha - cra que es her - mo - sa.

El po - lli - to goes like this: (peep peep)
El po - lli - to hace a - sí: (pió pió)

El po - lli - to goes like this (peep peep)
El po - lli - to hace a - sí: (pió pió)

Refrain

O vas, cam - a - rad - a, vas cam - a - rad - a, vas, O vas, O vas,

O vas, cam-a-rad-a, vas, cam-a-rad-a, vas, O vas, O vas.

2. El perrito goes like this: bow-bow
   (hace así: guau-guau)

3. El gatito goes like this: mee-ow
   (hace así: mi-au)

4. El burrito goes like this: hee-haw
   (hace así: ji-jo)

5. El patito goes like this: quack quack
   (hace así: cua cua)

6. El chanchito goes like this: oink oink
   (hace así: oinc oinc)

Help the children select rhythm instruments to imitate the sound of each animal on the farm.

Key: G major
Starting tone: G
Autoharp introduction: GG/D₇G
Beats per measure: 2/♩.

Pony Song

Words and music by Alice G. Thorn and Satis Coleman

See the po-ny gal-lop-ing, gal-lop-ing down the coun-try road.

Slow to end   *rit.*

See the po-ny com-ing home, all tired out, all tired out.

Ask the children to play the following pattern on two different size tone blocks, coconut shells, or the open ends of two paper cups hit together:

Key: D major (C major)
Starting tone: F♯ (E)
Autoharp introduction: (CC/G₇C) See below.
Beats per measure: 2/♩

Leading the Cows

Words paraphrased by V. S. Burrington
French Folk Song

Refrain

Slowly Lead - ing home the la - zy cows from pas - ture in the eve - ning,

Lead - ing home the la - zy cows, I sing as I lead them home.

Verse

1. The Jer - sey cows ___ have coats of brown, ___
2. The Hol - stein cows ___ are white and black, ___

Doo - dle doo - dle doo - dle down. ___
Loo loo loo, and a lack lack lack. ___

Make up additional verses similar to these with the class:
   The brown Swiss cows are shaded gray,
   Doodle, doodle, doodle day.
   The Guernsey cows are brown and white,
   Loo loo loo, and lack a light.

Have the children play the uneven rhythm pattern in this song on sticks or a wood block each time it is sung in the refrain: ²₄ ♫ ♪♫ ‖

The verse could be used for solo singing with a child choosing one of the verses here or creating another about a different kind of cow.

Key: C major
Starting tone: E
Autoharp introduction: CC/G₇C
Beats per measure: 2/♩

Feeding Time

Folk Song from Alabama
Collected by Mae Erskine Irvine

2. Little girl, little girl, Yes, sir.
   Did you feed my cat? Yes, sir.
   What did you feed it? Bread and milk,
   What did you feed it? Bread and milk.
3. Little boy, little boy, Yes, sir.
   Did you feed my horse? Yes, sir.

   What did you feed it? Corn and hay,
   What did you feed it? Corn and hay.
4. Little boy, little boy, Yes, sir.
   Did you feed my sheep? Yes, sir.
   What did you feed 'em? Oats and barley,
   What did you feed 'em? Oats and barley.

Choose a girl for each "little girl" verse and a boy for each "little boy" verse. Have the class ask the questions and the girl or boy for each verse answer them. Encourage the children to make up additional verses.

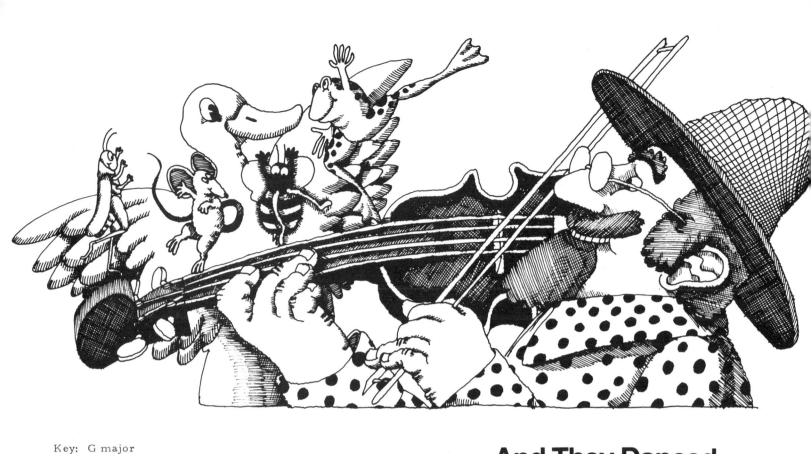

Key: G major
Starting tone: D
Autoharp introduction: GG/D₇G
Beats per measure: 4/♩

And They Danced

Words and music by Clara E. Spelman

Gaily

A fid-dler picked up his bow one day, And he fid-dled a-way, He

fid-dled a-way, And he fid-dled and he fid-dled a - way.

1. A duck heard him play so the duck be-gan to say,
2. A mouse heard him play so the mouse be-gan to say,
3. A frog heard him play so the frog be-gan to say,
4. A cricket heard him play so the cricket be-gan to say,
5. A bee heard him play so the bee be-gan to say,

From *Music in Our Town, Music for Living Series* © 1956, 1962 Silver Burdett Company. Reprinted by permission.

Take advantage of the opportunity to stress the difference between high and low sounds. Ask the children to exaggerate the highness of the high animal sounds and the lowness of the low animal sounds. Help them play the patterns on bells or the piano to feel the octave difference. Have individual children pretend to be each of the animals and sing the animal's sound as a solo.

The Grasshopper and the Ants

A story to dramatize by Louise Macbride

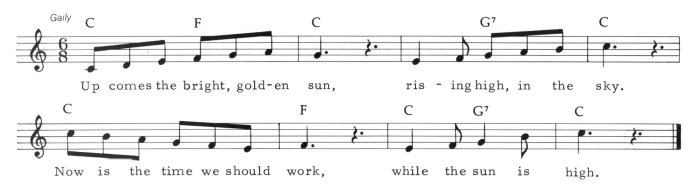

Up comes the bright, gold-en sun, ris - ing high, in the sky.

Now is the time we should work, while the sun is high.

At the edge of a wheat field, a group of ants were working.
Each ant carried a load of grain to the storehouse so
there would be enough to eat during the long, cold winter.
Back and forth they went, and, as they worked, they sang.

Work, work, work to-day. Now is the time for us to make hay.

Work, work, work with the sun. Soon we'll find our work is done.

A grasshopper came hopping by
and laughed at the busy ants.
"Ho! Ho! Ho! Only silly people
work on such a beautiful day.
Why are you working so hard?"

"In the winter," said one ant,
"when the ground is cold and frozen,
it will be difficult to find food.
That is why we gather our food
in the bright, warm sunshine."

It's such a love-ly day, to hop and play. You real-ly ought to stop, to play and hop.

From *Growing with Music Kindergarten Related Arts Edition* by Harry R. Wilson, Walter Ehret, Alice M. Knuth, Edward J. Hermann, Albert A. Renna © 1972 by Prentice-Hall, Inc., Englewood Cliffs, N.J. Reprinted by permission.

"We have work to do," said another ant, as he put a load of wheat on his back. "We shall think about hopping and playing when we have finished our work."

"Oh, bother!" said the grasshopper. "There is always time for work. Who wants to work on a nice day like this?"

"You'll see," said an ant. "When it is cold and stormy, we shall have plenty to eat because we gather our food now."

"Fiddle-dee-dee!" said the grasshopper. "Why worry about the winter now? All I want to do is hop and sing and play." And away he hopped, over the hill.

The ants said nothing, but continued working. Back and forth they went, carrying food from the wheat field to their storehouse.

Work, work, work to day. Now is the time for us to make hay.

Work, work, work with the sun. Soon we'll find our work is done.

As the days grew colder, the North Wind blew over the fields and whistled down the hills.

Ooo

The ants did not see the grasshopper again until one cold, winter night. There was a knock on the storehouse door, and, when they opened it, who should be standing there, shivering and hungry, but the grasshopper.

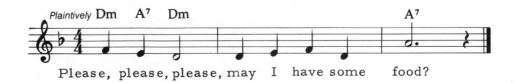

Please, please, please, may I have some food?

The ant at the door asked, "What were you doing
all summer, when we were busy working?"

"Oh, I was busy, too," said the shivering grasshopper.
"I sang and hopped and played all day long."

If you hopped all summer, you bet-ter hop now, for it is cold this win-ter day.

You can hop all win-ter, to keep yourself warm, Oh, Mister Grasshopper, go away.

The ant slammed the door with a bang.
The other ants laughed and laughed
as the poor grasshopper slowly walked away.

"Mister Grasshopper doesn't feel much like
singing and hopping now," said one of the ants.
"Look at him. I'll bet he wishes now that
he had worked last summer and gathered his food."

Work, work, when you're done, You'll have plenty of time for fun.

Key: F major
Starting tone: C
Autoharp introduction: FF/C₇F
Beats per measure: 4/♩

Five Little Kittens

Words and music by Charlotte G. Garman

2. Four little kittens running up a tree, One ran away and then there were three.
3. Three little kittens playing peek-a-boo, One ran away and then there were two.
4. Two little kittens sleeping in the sun, One ran away and then there was one.
5. One little kitten jumping up and down, It ran away and then there was none!

Introduce this counting song with numbers and kitten cutouts on a flannel board. Help the children dramatize the song.

Key: C major
Starting tone: C
Autoharp introduction: CC/G₇C
Beats per measure: 4/♩

Japanese Folk Song

This song is about some badgers who live in the mountains of Japan. Each morning they come out and look down the mountainside at some priests in a Buddhist temple. When the priests beat on their drums, the badgers beat on their tummies. The "Pon poko pon no pon" part of the A section is where the badgers pretend to beat on drums.

To emphasize the sameness of the A sections, have the children play drums on the underlying beat while they sing the A section and a contrasting instrument (jingle bells) for B.

Down by the River, Down by the Sea

A Big Turtle

A big turtle sat on the end of a log,
Watching a tadpole turn into a frog.

Unknown

Key: F major
Starting tone: C
Autoharp introduction: FF/C_7F
Beats per measure: 4/♩

Little White Duck

Words by Bernard Zaritzky
Music by Walt Barrows

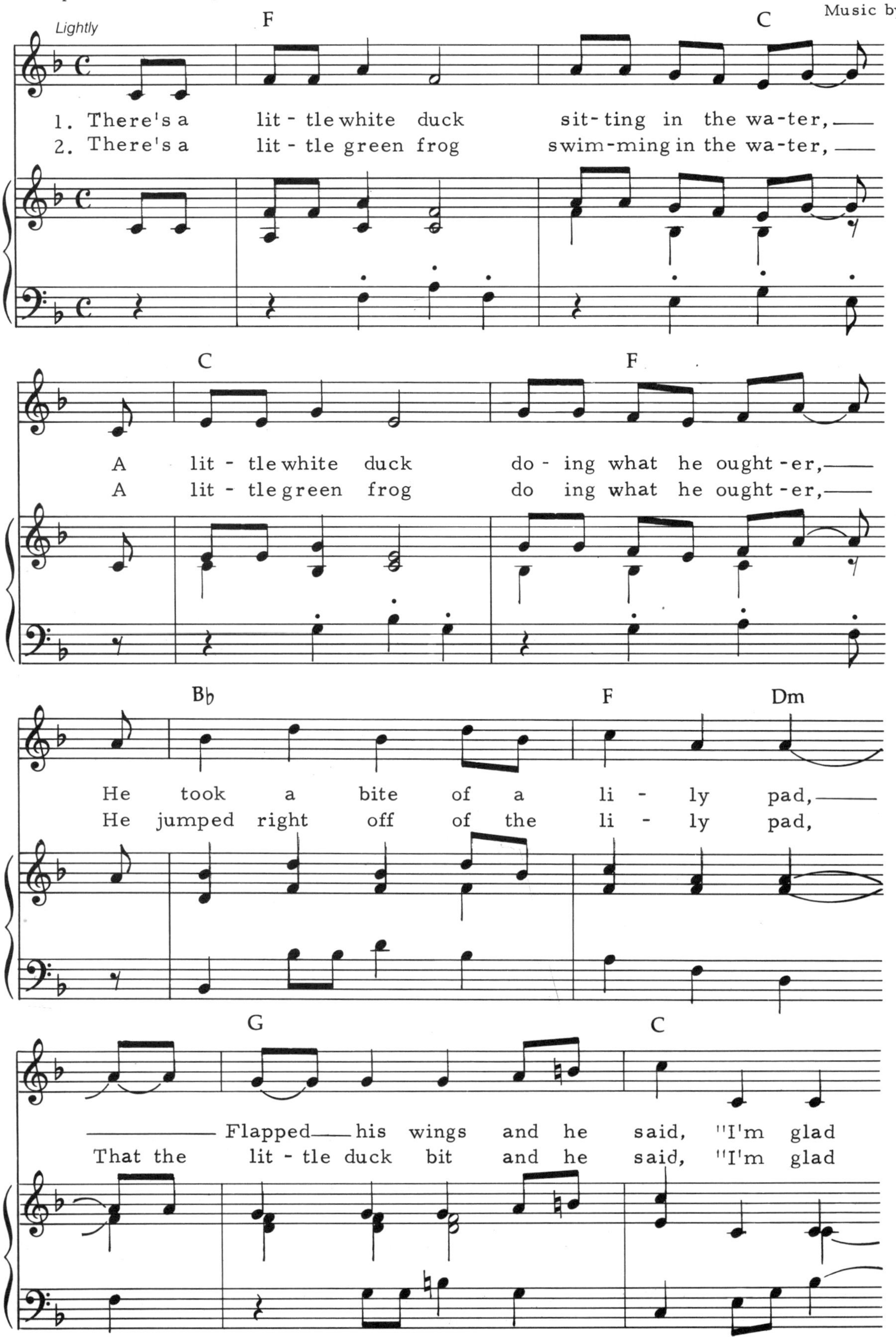
Lightly
F
C
1. There's a lit - tle white duck sit- ting in the wa-ter,
2. There's a lit - tle green frog swim-ming in the wa-ter,
C
F
A lit - tle white duck do - ing what he ought - er,
A lit - tle green frog do ing what he ought - er,
B♭
F
Dm
He took a bite of a li - ly pad,
He jumped right off of the li - ly pad,
G
C
Flapped his wings and he said, "I'm glad
That the lit - tle duck bit and he said, "I'm glad

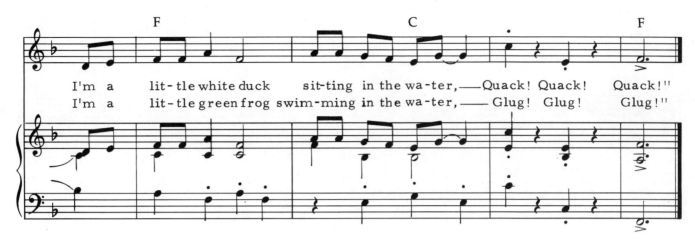

I'm a lit-tle white duck sit-ting in the wa-ter,——Quack! Quack! Quack!"

I'm a lit-tle green frog swim-ming in the wa-ter,—— Glug! Glug! Glug!"

3. There's a little black bug floating on the water,
   A little black bug doing what he oughter,
   He tickled the frog on the lily pad,
   That the little duck bit and he said, "I'm glad
   I'm a little black bug floating on the water.
   Bzz! Bzz! Bzz!"

4. There's a little red snake playing in the water,
   A little red snake doing what he oughter,
   He frightened the duck and the frog so bad,
   He ate the bug and he said, "I'm glad
   I'm a little red snake playing in the water.
   Hiss! Hiss! Hiss!"

5. Now there's nobody left sitting in the water,
   Nobody left doing what he oughter,
   There's nothing left but the lily pad,
   The duck and the frog ran away; I'm sad
   'Cause there's nobody left sitting in the water.
   Boo! Hoo! Hoo!

Have the children work with figures on a flannel board to tell this story. They may also act out the song with hand motions or with body movement. The last verse should be sung slowly and sadly. Ask different children to take the parts of the duck, the frog, the bug, and the snake and sing from "I'm glad" to the end as a solo.

Key: F major
Starting tone: A
Autoharp introduction: FF/C₇F
Beats per measure: 2/♩

Six Little Ducks

American Folk Song

1. Six lit-tle ducks that I once knew, Fat ones, skin-ny ones,
2. Down to the riv-er they would go, Wib-ble wob-ble, wib-ble wob-ble,
3. Home from the riv-er they would come, Wib-ble wob-ble, wib-ble wob-ble,

fair ones too,
ho-hum-ho, } But the one lit-tle duck with the feath-er in his back,
ho-hum-hum,

He ruled the oth-ers with a quack, quack, quack, quack, quack, quack,

quack, quack, quack, He ruled the oth-ers with a quack, quack, quack.

Encourage the children to create hand motions for the words of the song. Help them explore the sounds of five or six rhythm instruments to find out what could imitate the "quack, quack, quack" (guiro or notched sticks). Suggest that they sing the quacks inside their heads while the instrument plays and be ready to sing the next phrase out loud.

From *Growing with Music Book I Related Arts Edition* by Harry R. Wilson, Walter Ehret, Alice M. Knuth, Edward J. Hermann, Albert A. Renna © 1970 by Prentice-Hall, Inc., Englewood Cliffs, N.J. Reprinted by permission.

Key: D major (C major)
Starting tone: A (G)
Autoharp introduction: (CC/CC) See below.
Beats per measure: 2/♩

Ten Little Frogs

Words by Louise B. Scott
Music by Virginia Parelko

1. Ten lit - tle speck-led frogs, Sat on —— a speck-led log,
2. Nine

Catch -ing—— some most de - li -cious bugs, yum, yum,

One jumped—— in - to the pool, Where it —— was nice and cool,

And there — were nine green speck-led frogs, glub, glub.
eight

Last verse:
    One little speckled frog, Sat on a speckled log,
    Catching some most delicious bugs, yum, yum,
    He jumped into the pool, Where it was nice and cool,
    And there were no green speckled frogs, glub, glub.

Let the children use their fingers to help count backward. If ten is too many, begin with five frogs. Use rhythm instruments for sound effects for the "yum, yum" and "glub, glub."

Key: F major
Starting tone: F
Autoharp introduction: FF/C$_7$F
Beats per measure: 4/♩

A Lizard and a Frog

Words and music by Patricia T. Pinkston

Easy calypso

Oh I found a liz - ard and I found a frog,

And a go - pher hid - ing un - der - neath a log,

And I tell you what ___ I think is fun to do,

I think that we can start a zoo.

With a box for the liz - ard and a cage for the frog,

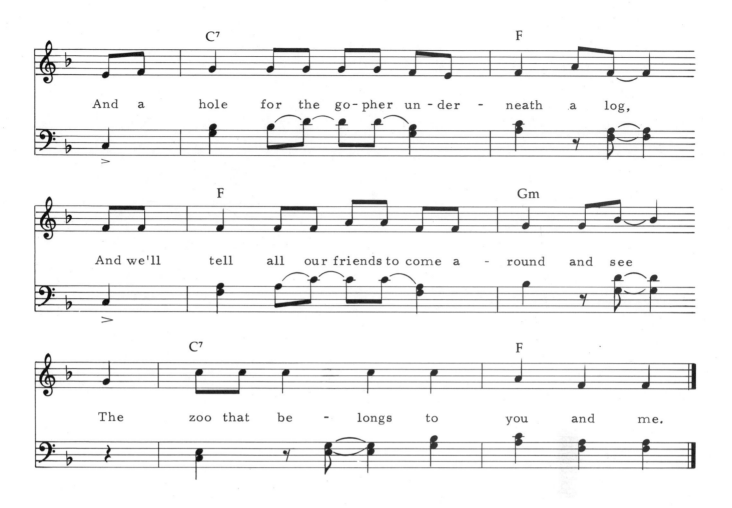

And a hole for the go-pher un-der - neath a log,

And we'll tell all our friends to come a - round and see

The zoo that be - longs to you and me.

Any of the following patterns may be played over and over again as an accompaniment on bells or piano:

Help the children choose a rhythm instrument for each animal and set up an accompaniment pattern alternating the instruments. For example, use the following rhythm pattern:

Repeat the four measures for the duration of the song.

lizard
instrument

frog
instrument

gopher
instrument

all together

Key: C major
Starting tone: G
Autoharp introduction: CC/G₇C
Beats per measure: 2/♩

I Had a Little Turtle

Words by Vachel Lindsay
Music by Satis N. Coleman

Not too fast

There was a lit - tle tur - tle Who lived in a box;

He swam in a pud - dle, He climbed on the rocks.

He snapped at a mos - qui - to, He snapped at a flea,

He snapped at a min - now, He snapped at me.

He caught the mos - qui - to, He caught the flea,

He caught the min - now, But he did - n't catch me!

With a "shell" to tie on the back of the "turtle" and pictures to represent the mosquito, the flea, and the minnow, the children may readily dramatize this song. Help the children learn the song by using a cardboard arrow or similar prop to underscore the direction of the beginning of each two-measure section.

The Bold Fisherman

Key: F major
Starting tone: C
Autoharp introduction: FFF/FFF
Beats per measure: 3/♩

Sea Chantey

Verse *Happily*

There was a bold fish-er-man who sail'd out from Pim-be-co,

To slay the wild cod-fish and bold mack-'ral too.

When he ar-rived off Pim-be-co the storm-y winds did wild-ly blow,

His lit-tle boat went wib-blewob-ble and o-ver-board went he,

Refrain

Sing-ing twin-ka-doo-dle-dum, twin-ka-doo-dle-dum, The

118

high - ly in - ter - est - ing song he sang, Twin - ka - doo - dle - dum,

twin - ka - doo - dle - dum, sang the fish - er - man.

Ask the children to find the nonsense words in this song. Then have one child or a small group of children sing the melodic pattern of "twinka-doodle-dum."

The underlying beat of this song is strong and is grouped in three**s**. Ask the children to listen for the grouping. Then have them play the accented beat on sticks or wood blocks and the underlying beat on sand blocks or jingle bells.

Who Did?

Key: F major
Starting tone: F
Autoharp introduction: FF/C₇ F
Beats per measure: 2/♩

Gaily

1st voice / 2nd voice — 1st / 2nd — Both

1. Who did? Who did? Who did swal-low Jo - Jo - Jo - Jo?
2. Whale did, Who did? Whale did, Who did? Whale did swal-low Jo - Jo - Jo - Jo,
   Whale did, Whale did,

1st / 2nd — 1st / 2nd — Both

Who did? Who did? Who did swal-low Jo - Jo — Jo - Jo?
Whale did, Who did? Whale did, Who did? Whale did swal-low Jo - Jo — Jo — Jo,
Whale did, Whale did,

The pattern for the question "Who did?" occurs in three places in this song. The first and third are identical, but the second begins higher. Let the children make this discovery for themselves. Ask them to play the patterns on bells.

Divide the class into two groups and follow the directions on the music as to which group sings when. Help the children make up additional verses to the song.

Key: G major
Starting tone: D
Autoharp introduction: GG/D₇G
Beats per measure: 4/♩

The Allee-Allee O

Traditional

Oh, the big ship's a-sail-ing through the Al-lee-Al-lee O,

the Al-lee-Al-lee O, the Al-lee-Al-lee O!

Oh, the big ship's a-sail-ing through the Al-lee-Al-lee O!

Hi, Ding-dong dair!

The Allee is a channel between large rocks off the coast of Maine. Children in lines form the channel. Other children take turns being a big ship, which sails through the channel.

Help the children make up additional verses to this song:
The little tug is chugging through the Allee-Allee O . . .
The sailboat is gliding through the . . .
The bell buoy is dinging in the . . .
The sea gulls are flying over the . . .

Encourage the children to sing slowly and heavily for the big ship, faster and lighter for the little tug, etc.

Make a chart in blank notation for the melodic patterns of the words "Allee-Allee O." Then ask, "Which pattern is first in the song? Which is last? Which is second? Which is heard twice?"

1. _____ _____

3. _____ _____ _____ _____

_____ _____ _____ _____

_____ _____

2. _____ _____ _____ _____

From Growing with Music Kindergarten Related Arts Edition by Harry R. Wilson, Walter Ehret, Alice M. Knuth, Edward J. Hermann, Albert A. Renna © 1972 by Prentice-Hall, Inc., Englewood Cliffs, N.J. Reprinted by permission.

Key: D minor
Starting tone: A
Autoharp introduction: DmDm/AmDm
Beats per measure: 4/♩

Sailing Song

Sea Chantey

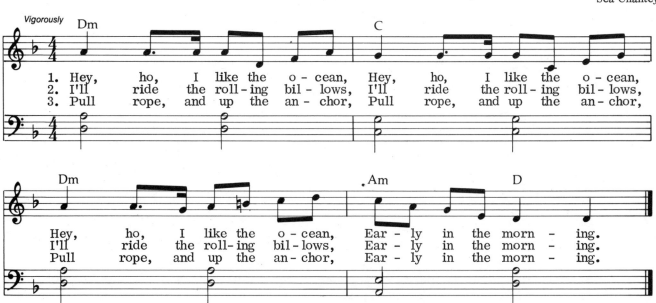

Vigorously

1. Hey, ho, I like the o - cean, Hey, ho, I like the o - cean,
2. I'll ride the roll- ing bil- lows, I'll ride the roll- ing bil- lows,
3. Pull rope, and up the an - chor, Pull rope, and up the an- chor,

Hey, ho, I like the o - cean, Ear - ly in the morn - ing.
I'll ride the roll- ing bil- lows, Ear - ly in the morn - ing.
Pull rope, and up the an - chor, Ear - ly in the morn - ing.

Explain that sailors on sailing ships often sang songs like this one as they did their work. Suggest that the children dramatize the song by pretending to do various tasks, such as pulling on a rope to bring up the ship's anchor or scrubbing the deck of the ship.

Key: C major
Starting tone: G
Autoharp introduction: CC/G₇C
Beats per measure: 4/♩

The Jolly Sailor

Words by Mary Malthes
Chantey Ballad

A life most jol - ly is the life at sea.

The salt spray fly - ing when the wind blows free.

The whale is spout - ing as he goes be - low,

And the cap - tain's jol - ly, so it's yo, heave ho!

This song may be accompanied with a single-tone ostinato on bells or piano or with voices. Keep repeating this pattern for the duration of the song:

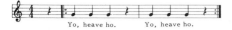

Yo, heave ho.   Yo, heave ho.

124

Key: G minor
Starting tone: D
Autoharp introduction: Gm Gm / D₇ Gm
Beats per measure: 4/♩

Pirate Crew

Words by Marchette Gaylord Chute
Music by Ruth McCann Spencer

Help the children see the whimsical nature of this song. Ask them to find the octave jump downward in the song. Then use that pattern as a bell ostinato accompaniment throughout the song:

Keep repeating the pattern.

Let's Go to the Zoo

Early Morning at the Zoo

Monkeys stretch and scratch and yawn,
Peacocks scream and wake the fawn,
Lions wake up with a roar,
Tigers give a startled snore,
Seals are hungry, ducks are too—
It's early morning at the zoo.

Helen M. Webster

Key: C major
Starting tone: G
Autoharp introduction: CCCC/
Beats per measure: 4/♩

The Children's Zoo

Words and music by Lucille Wood

1. How do you do? How do you do? We are glad to see you.
2. I am a duck, I am a duck, I am glad to see you.
3. I am a hen, I am a hen, I am glad to see you.

1. How do you do? How do you do? We are glad to see you.
2. I am a duck, I am a duck, I am glad to see you.
3. I am a hen, I am a hen, I am glad to see you.

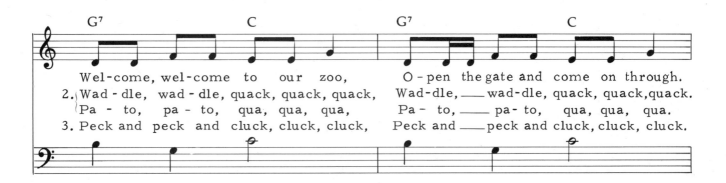

Wel-come, wel-come to our zoo, O-pen the gate and come on through.
2. Wad-dle, wad-dle, quack, quack, quack, Wad-dle,___ wad-dle, quack, quack, quack.
Pa-to, pa-to, qua, qua, qua, Pa-to,___ pa-to, qua, qua, qua.
3. Peck and peck and cluck, cluck, cluck, Peck and ___ peck and cluck, cluck, cluck.

How do you do? How do you do? We are glad to see you.
I am a duck, I am a duck, I am glad to see you.
I am a hen, I am a hen, I am glad to see you.

In this song the music and the words are the same for phrases one, two, and four. Therefore, the children can readily identify the like and unlike phrases. Ask them to perform like movements for the A phrases and a different movement for B or to play the same instrument for the A phrases (perhaps a drum) and a different one for B (perhaps a guiro or notched stick for the duck verse, wood block for the hen verse, etc.) Ask the children to create verses about other animals. They may substitute animal names in other languages as well as English.

Key: F major
Starting tone: F
Autoharp introduction: FF/C₇F
Beats per measure: 2/♩

I Can't Spell Hippopotamus

Words and music by J. Fred Coots

I can spell "Hat", "H - A - T", I can spell "Cat", "C - A - T",
I can spell "Top", "T - O - P", I can spell "Hop", "H - O - P",

I can spell "Fat", "F - A - T", But I can't spell Hip-po - pot-a-mus.
I can spell "Mop", "M - O - P", But I can't spell Hip-po - pot-a-mus.

"H - I - P-P-O" I know, and then comes "P-O - T",

But that's as far as I can go, and that's what both-ers me, Gee!

I can spell "Dog", "D - O - G", I can spell "Log", "L - O - G",

128

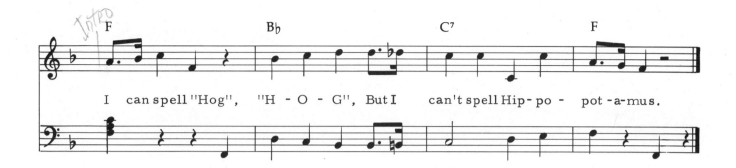

I can spell "Hog", "H - O - G", But I can't spell Hip-po- pot-a-mus.

Encourage the children to think of other groups of three-letter rhyming words from which they can create new verses for the song. The three-note ascending patterns for the spelling of each word present good opportunities for solo singing. Have the class sing the song while volunteers sing "H-A-T." "C-A-T," and "F-A-T" as solos. The ABA form of the song lends itself to small groups on the B section and the whole class on the A sections.

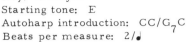

Key: C major
Starting tone: E
Autoharp introduction: CC/G₇C
Beats per measure: 2/♩

Animal Song

Folk Song from Michigan

1. Al-li-ga-tor, hedge-hog, ant-eat-er, bear, Rat-tle-snake, buf-fa-lo, an-a-con-da, hare.

2. Bullfrog, woodchuck, wolverine, goose,
   Whippoorwill, chipmunk, jackal, moose.
3. Mud turtle, whale, glow-worm, bat,
   Salamander, snail, and Maltese cat.
4. Black squirrel, coon, opossum, wren,
   Red squirrel, loon, South Guinea hen.
5. Polecat, dog, wild otter, rat,
   Pelican, hog, dodo, and bat.

6. Eagle, kingeron, sheep, duck, and widgeon,
   Conger, armadillo, beaver, seal, pigeon.
7. Reindeer, blacksnake, ibex, nightingale,
   Martin, wild drake, crocodile, and quail.
8. House rat, toe rat, white bear, doe,
   Chickadee, peacock, bobolink, and crow.

Use letter clues to help the children remember the sequence of animals in each verse. Encourage the children to create a verse or two of their own, ending each two-measure group of animals with names that rhyme.

Key: A minor
Starting tone: A
Autoharp introduction: Am Am/Am Am
Beats per measure: 2/♩.

The Camel

Words and music by Gladys Tipton

Emphasize the uneven sway of the camel by letting the children play the following rhythm pattern throughout the song on tone blocks, coconut shells, or the open ends of two paper cups struck together:

Ask some of the children to imitate the camel's walk while others sing the song.

Key: G major
Starting tone: G
Autoharp introduction: GG/D7G
Beats per measure: 4/♩

Ollie in the Forest

English words by Kate Cox Goddard
Swedish Folk Song

Moderately

1. Ol - lie's a-lone in the for - est brown;
2. "Gruff, ruff ruff ruff," What is that, what is that?

Flow'rs look-ing up and trees look-ing down,
"Gruff, ruff ruff ruff," Not a dog, not a cat!

Brook - let a-laugh-ing to
No, it's a bear with ——

see Ol - lie play,
long shag-gy hair!

Birds, sing-ing clear, make the brown for-est gay.
"Come let us play, Mis-ter Bear, Mis-ter Bear."

3. Pat, pat-pat-pat! Ollie pats his head,
   Bear looks at Ollie, hopes he'll be fed;
   Bear eats some berries and looks all around,
   Finding the ones Ollie spilled on the ground.

4. "Ollie, it's Mother, where have you been?"
   Bear looks at Mother and runs for his den!
   "Why, Mother, why did you scare him away?
   Please ask the bear to come back here and play."

The idea of making friends with wild animals is appealing to children. Ask them to dramatize this story. Help them understand the difference between the narrative parts of the song and the dialogue parts. Have the whole class sing the narrative while individual children sing the lines that Ollie, the bear, and Mother sing. A few simple props (a kerchief for Mother, some long shaggy hair for the bear, and a basket for Ollie to carry) will enhance the dramatization.

Key: D minor
Starting tone: D
Autoharp introduction: DmDm/AmDm
Beats per measure: 4/♩

Leo, the Lion

Words and music by Vic Marantz

Have the children experiment with using loud singing (not yelling) voices on this song. Play a simple ostinato on the piano with an interruption at the end of each phrase for an appropriate "roar" on the lowest piano keys.

Play an octave or two lower and keep repeating throughout the song, with interruptions for the "roar."

Accompaniment on a large drum with either or both of the following patterns would also add to the mood of the song.

Key: G major
Starting tone: D
Autoharp introduction: GG/D₇G
Beats per measure: 2/♩.

One More River

American Negro

Verse *Not too fast*

1. Old No-ah built him-self an ark. One more riv-er to cross._____
2. The an-i-mals came two by two. One more riv-er to cross._____
3. The an-i-mals came three by three. One more riv-er to cross._____

He built it out of hick-'ry bark. One more riv-er to cross._____
The el-e-phant and kan-ga-roo. One more riv-er to cross._____
The ba-boon and the chim-pan-zee. One more riv-er to cross._____

Refrain

One more riv-er, And that wide riv-er is Jor-dan,

One more riv-er, There's one more riv-er to cross._____

The following verses could be added or others created by the children:

four by four . . . The hippopotamus stuck in the door.
five by five . . . The bees came swarming from the hive.
six by six . . . The moneky doin' his monkey tricks.
seven by seven . . . The lion hollered, "Quit that shovin'."

Key: C major
Starting tone: E
Autoharp introduction: CC/G$_7$C
Beats per measure: 2/♩.

The Animal Fair

Traditional

With humor

I went to the an-i-mal fair, ___ The birds and the beasts were there. ___

The old rac-coon by the light of the moon Was comb-ing her au-burn hair. ___

The fun-ni-est was the monk, ___ He climbed up the el-e-phant's trunk, ___

The el-e-phant sneezed and fell on his knees, And what be-came of the monk? ___

Suggested bell, piano, or vocal ostinato:

The monk, the monk, the monk, the monk

Help the children find the following melodic pattern in the song; E G G G A A E G

Ask one child to play the pattern on the resonator bells each time it is sung in the song.

Over the Hills and through the Woods

Rain

The rain is raining all around,
  It falls on field and tree,
It rains on the umbrellas here,
  And on the ships at sea.

Robert Louis Stevenson

Key: C major
Starting tone: G
Autoharp introduction: C/Am/G₇/C
Beats per measure: 3/♪

I'm Glad

Traditional words
Music by Carl Fredrickson

I'm glad the sky is paint - ed blue,

And earth is paint - ed green, ____

With such a lot of nice fresh air

All sand - wiched in be - tween. ____

Have some of the children try tapping the underlying beat of the song (1-2-3) while the others clap the rhythm of the words or the melodic rhythm. Transfer both patterns to different rhythm instruments.

From *Growing with Music Book 1 Related Arts Edition* by Harry R. Wilson, Walter Ehret, Alice M. Knuth, Edward J. Hermann, Albert A. Renna ©1970 by Prentice-Hall, Inc., Englewood Cliffs, N.J. Reprinted by permission.

The First Tulip

Key: C major
Starting tone: C
Autoharp introduction: CG_7/CC
Beats per measure: 4/♩

Words and music by Elinor Westbrook

Here look in the gar-den bed;
Last night it was small and green;

Some-thing beau-ti-ful is grow - ing!
Flame-like now it is a-glow - ing!

Bright, shaped like a cup all red,
This one is the first I've seen,

Tu - lip o-pens to the sun.
Now sweet weath-er is be - gun.

Use a chart of the melodic contour of the melody and have the children draw the shape of it in the air as they sing the song.

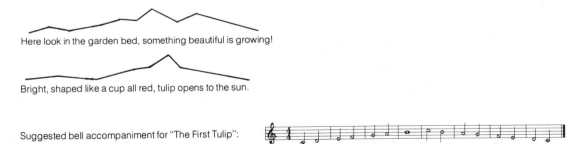

Here look in the garden bed, something beautiful is growing!

Bright, shaped like a cup all red, tulip opens to the sun.

Suggested bell accompaniment for "The First Tulip":

Key: C major
Starting tone: C
Autoharp introduction: CC/G_7C
Beats per measure: 4/♩

Popcorn Popping

Words by Georgia W. Bello
Music by Betty Lou Cooney

I looked out the win-dow and what did I see?

Pop-corn pop-ping on the ap-ri-cot tree!

Spring had brought me such a nice sur-prise

Blos-soms pop-ping right be-fore my eyes.

I could take an arm-ful and make a treat,

A pop - corn ball that would smell so sweet. It was - n't real - ly so,

but it seemed to be ———— pop - corn pop - ping on the ap - ri - cot tree.

To help the children learn this long, rather wordy song, have them make up hand motions for each short phrase. Let them discover which two phrases are exactly alike (second and last) and which one is similar (fourth).

Key: G major
Starting tone: B
Autoharp introduction: GGG/GGG
Beats per measure: 3/♩

Apple Tree Is Blooming

Words and music by Charlotte G. Garman

1. Ap - ple tree is bloom - ing, ———— In her dress so gay, ————

Ap - ple tree is bloom - ing, ————'Tis the month of May.

2. Butterfly is winging, Happy in her play,
   Butterfly is winging, 'Tis the month of May.
3. Bee is busy humming, Working all the day,
   Bee is busy humming, 'Tis the month of May.

Call the children's attention to the rhythm pattern of the first measure: ¾ ♩. ♪ ♩ ♩ |
Have the children count how many times they hear it in the song. Then let them play it on a rhythm instrument (perhaps sticks) each time it occurs in the song.

Key: D major (C major)
Starting tone: A (G)
Autoharp introduction: (CC/G₇C) See below.
Beats per measure: 2/♩

Give, Said the Little Stream

Verse *Not too slow*

1. Give, said the lit - tle stream, Give, oh! give, give, oh! give,
2. Give, said the lit - tle rain, Give, oh! give, give, oh! give,
3. Give, then what you can give; Give, oh! give, give, oh! give.

Give, said the lit - tle stream, As it hur - ried down the hill;
Give, said the lit - tle rain As it fell up - on the flow'rs.
Give, then what you can give; There is some - thing all can give.

I'm small I know, but wher - ev - er I go, The fields grow green - er still.
I'll raise their droop - ing heads a - gain, As it fell up - on the flow'rs.
Do as the streams and blos - soms do, And for oth - er peo - ple live.

Refrain

Sing - ing, sing - ing all the day, Give a - way, oh! give a - way.

Sing - ing, sing - ing all the day, Give, oh! give a - way.

This song is a good example of a verse-refrain song. Help the children become familiar with the idea that the verses change but that the refrain is the same each time. Have the boys sing the verses and the girls the refrain. Then ask them to switch parts.

140

Key: D major (C major)
Starting tone: F♯ (E)
Autoharp introduction: (CCC/CCC) See below.
Beats per measure: 3/♩

It Rained a Mist

Folk Song from Virginia

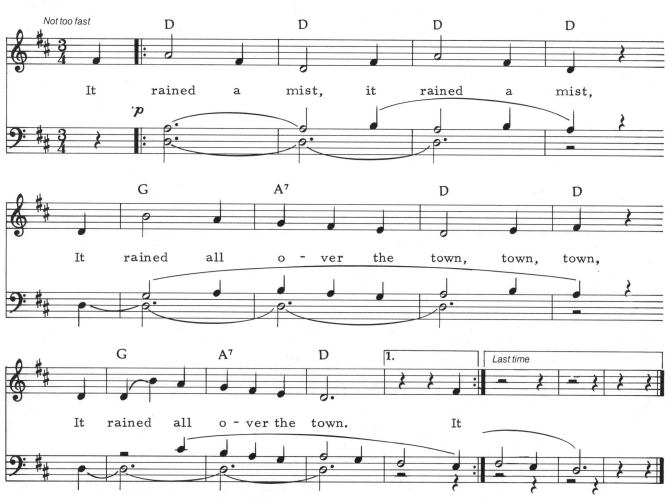

It rained a mist, it rained a mist,

It rained all o - ver the town, town, town,

It rained all o - ver the town.   It

Encourage the children to use their imaginations to create different verses about what the rain might be falling on: other places, other things, animals, and people.

141

Key: D minor
Starting tone: D
Autoharp introduction: Dm Dm/Dm Dm
Beats per measure: 4/♩

How Many Raindrops?

Words and music by Trudi Behar

Pit-ter, pat-ter, pit-ter, pat, See the rain-drops come, fall-ing one by one.

How man-y rain-drops make a storm? One lit-tle rain-drop? No, no, no!

Two lit-tle rain-drops? No, no, no! Three lit-tle rain-drops? No, no, no!

Four lit-tle rain-drops? No, no, no! Five lit-tle rain-drops? No, no, no!

Mil-lions of rain-drops make a storm! Bil-lions of rain-drops make a storm!

Pit - ter, pat - ter, pit - ter, pat, See the rain-drops come, fall-ing one by one.

Suggested bell or piano accompaniment: Keep repeating the pattern.

Encourage the children to add some sound effects with sticks or tapped pencils throughout the song.

Have the children count raindrops on their fingers. Ask individual children to try the single-chord accompaniment for this song on the Autoharp.

Key: Pentatonic—D, F, G, A, C
Starting tone: D
Autoharp introduction: Dm Dm/Dm Dm
Beats per measure: 4/♩

Rain Song

Yuma Indian Song

1. Hear, Great Spir-it, corn is dy-ing. Hear, Great Spir-it, corn is dy-ing.
2. Hear, Great Spir-it, send us rain clouds. Hear, Great Spir-it, send us rain clouds.

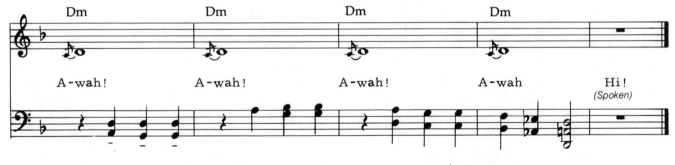

A-wah!   A-wah!   A-wah!   A-wah   Hi!
(Spoken)

Let one child accompany the song at the piano, playing A and D together twice in each measure.

If the five tones of the pentatonic scale (see "Key" above) are made sharp, then the whole melody may be played on the black keys of the piano. The children may then improvise any accompaniment pattern as long as they play only on the black keys.

Large drum accompaniment:

Small drum accompaniment:

Shake rattles on "A-wah!"

Key: C major
Starting tone: C
Autoharp introduction: CC/G₇C
Beats per measure: 4/♩

The Tree in the Wood

Old English Cumulative Song

Verse *Lightly*

1. All in a wood there grew a tree,
2. And on this tree there grew a limb,

The fin - est tree you ev - er did see;
The fin - est limb you ev - er did see;

* The tree was in the wood And the
The limb was on the tree
The tree was in the wood

Refrain

green leaves grew all a - round, a - round, a - round,

And the green leaves grew all a - round.

3. And on this limb there was a branch
The finest branch you ever did see;
The branch was on the limb,
The limb was on the tree,
The tree was in the wood, etc.

4. And on this branch there was a nest, etc.
5. And in this nest there was an egg, etc.
6. And in this egg there was a bird, etc.
7. And on this bird there was a wing, etc.
8. And on this wing there was a feather, etc.

*In each verse, repeat, backward, all the lines naming objects, until you have sung "The tree was in the wood," then sing the refrain.

144

Key: F major
Starting tone: C
Autoharp introduction: FF/C₇F
Beats per measure: 4/♩

A Basketful of Nuts

Old Dutch Folk Song

With quick, light movement

1. A bas-ket-ful of nuts I've gath-ered from the wal-nut tree,
2. If you will come a - long, we'll get some more good nuts for you,

And now I'm go-ing home, and I am tak - ing them with me.
And you can throw some sticks or climb and shake the bran-ches too.

Fa la la, Fa la la, Fa la la la la la la la,

Fa la la, Fa la la, Fa la la la la la la la,

A bas-ket-ful of nuts I've gath-ered from the wal-nut tree.
Oh, noth-ing is more fun than nut-ting in the Fall with you.

In many areas of the world one of the favorite activities of the Fall is "nutting," or gathering nuts. Let the children play a simple ostinato on bells or piano throughout this song:

Use the ostinato as an introduction, as an interlude between verses, and as a coda.

Key: E♭ major (F major)
Starting tone: G (A)
Autoharp introduction: (FF/C₇F) See below.
Beats per measure: 4/♩

Hey, Mr. Echo

Words and music by Samuel C. Yahres

Cheerfully Teacher: Children: Teacher: Children:

1. Hey, Mis-ter Ech-o! Hey, Mis-ter Ech-o! High in the tree-top! High in the tree-top!

Teacher: Children: Teacher: Children:

Why are you sing-ing? Why are you sing-ing? All the day long! All the day long!

2. Is that your name, sir? (Is that your name, sir?)
   What is your answer? (What is your answer?)
   What is he saying? (What is he saying?)
   "Listen to me!" ("Listen to me!")

3. Dear Mister Echo. (Dear Mr. Echo.)
   Do you believe me? (Do you believe me?)
   I'm not an echo! (I'm not an echo!)
   I'm a big boy/girl! (I'm a big boy!/girl!)

Have some of the children sing the "teacher" part while the others sing the "children," or echo, part. Encourage the first group to sing (not yell) *forte* and the echo group to sing *pianissimo.*

Key: F major
Starting tone: C
Autoharp introduction: FFF/FFF
Beats per measure: 3/♩

Hear the Wind Blow

Words and music by Charlotte G. Garman

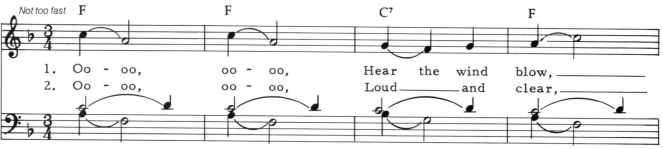

Not too fast F F C⁷ F

1. Oo - oo, oo - oo, Hear the wind blow, _____
2. Oo - oo, oo - oo, Loud _____ and clear, _____

F F C⁷ F *rit.*

Oo - oo, oo - oo, Where does it go?
Oo - oo, oo - oo, Right in my ear!

Use the two-tone pattern of the "oo-oo" as a tone call for individual children while the rest of the class sings the remainder of the song. Make the song more expressive by asking the children to begin the first phrase softly and make a crescendo to *forte* by the end of the word "blow." Then begin the second phrase loudly and make a diminuendo to *pianissimo* by the end of the song.

Key: F major
Starting tone: C
Autoharp introduction: FFF/FFF
Beats per measure: 3/♩

Words by George Cooper
Music by Patricia Haglund Nielsen

Slow waltz

1. "Come, lit - tle leaves," said the wind one day,

"Come o'er the mea - dows with me and play.

Put on your dress - es of red and gold,

For sum - mer is gone, and the days grow cold."

2. Soon as the leaves heard the wind's loud call,
   Down they came fluttering, one and all;
   Over the brown fields they danced and flew,
   Singing the sweet little songs they knew.

3. Dancing and whirling, the little leaves went,
   Winter had called them, and they were content.
   Soon, fast asleep in their earthy beds,
   The snow laid a coverlid over their heads.

Help the children focus their attention on the melodic pattern of the last two measures of each phrase by asking the following questions: Which one begins highest? Which one is lowest? Which pattern moves up instead of down?

Let the children use colored scarves and create a dance the leaves might do as they float in the wind.

Key: C major
Starting tone: C
Autoharp introduction: CCCC/
Beats per measure: 4/♩

Traditional

Suggested bell or piano accompaniment:

Use the word "scale" with the children in describing the up and down movement of the song and of the bell part.

I Love the Mountains

Traditional Song

Key: F major
Starting tone: F
Autoharp introduction: F / Dm / C₇ / F
Beats per measure: 4/♩

If the children are independent enough as singers, ask a small group to keep repeating the first two measures of the refrain throughout the whole song.

Play this pattern on the bells or on the piano as an introduction and also as a coda:

Play a drum lightly during the last five measures.

Key: G major
Starting tone: B
Autoharp introduction: GGGG/
Beats per measure: 4/♩

Sh-Sh, Snowflakes Falling

Words and music by Charlotte G. Garman

Gently

Sh - Sh Snow-flakes fall-ing, Fall-ing ve-ry still,——
(whisper)

Sh - Sh Snow-flakes fall - ing On my win-dow sill.——

Sh - Sh Snow-flakes fall - ing, Fall-ing here and there,——

Sh - Sh Snow-flakes fall - ing, Fall-ing ev'-ry-where.——

For the repeat, play both hands one octave higher. Help the children sing this song slowly, softly, and smoothly. Finger cymbals or a triangle played very lightly at the beginning of each measure will add to the mood of this song. Let some children pretend to be the gently falling snowflakes while others sing the song. Encourage them to use slow, smooth movements.

Happy Times

Happy Thought

The world is so full of a number of things,
I'm sure we should all be as happy as kings.

Robert Louis Stevenson

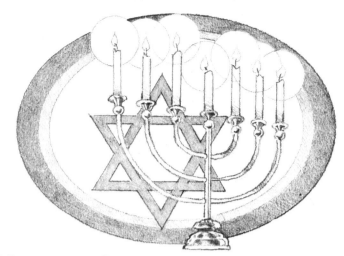

Key: D minor
Starting tone: E
Autoharp introduction: DmDm/DmDm
Beats per measure: 2/♩

Havenu Shalom Aleichem

Israeli Folk Song

The Hebrew text means "We bring you greetings of peace." The single word "shalom" is the traditional Hebrew greeting meaning "peace." It is used both for our "hello" and our "good-bye."

The underlying beat is strong and is grouped in twos. Have the children use the tambourine or finger cymbals on the accent and a drum on the underlying beat:

Tambourine or finger cymbals:

Drum:

Key: G minor
Starting tone: D
Autoharp introduction: GmGm/D₇Gm
Beats per measure: 4/♩

I'm Not Scared

Words and music by Lucille Wood

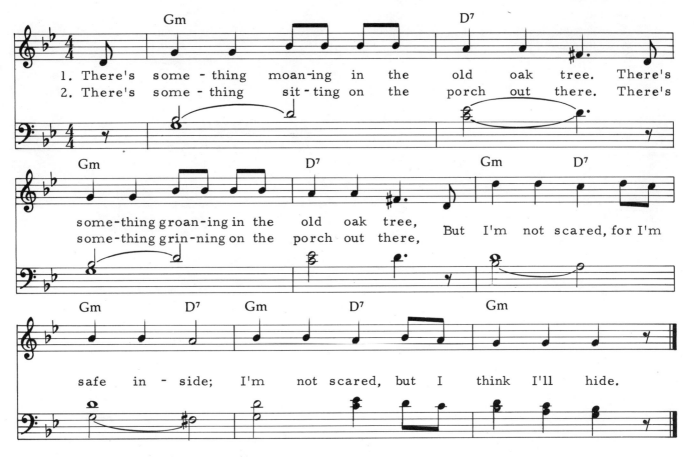

1. There's some - thing moan-ing in the old oak tree. There's
2. There's some - thing sit-ting on the porch out there. There's

some-thing groan-ing in the old oak tree, But I'm not scared, for I'm
some-thing grin-ning on the porch out there,

safe in - side; I'm not scared, but I think I'll hide.

3. There's something howling on the fence out there.
   There's something yowling on the fence out there,
   But I'm not scared, for I'm safe inside;
   I'm not scared, but I think I'll hide.

4. There's something flying through the air;
   On a broomstick, gliding through the air,
   But I'm not scared, for I'm safe inside;
   I'm not scared, but I think I'll hide.

The song becomes very dramatic through the use of dynamics. Let the children begin singing softly and mysteriously and make a gradual crescendo to the end of the first phrase. The first half of the second phrase should be sung confidently in a full voice and the second half suddenly much softer, with almost a whisper on "think I'll hide."

Key: F major
Starting tone: A
Autoharp introduction: FF/C₇F
Beats per measure: 4/♩

Halloween Is Coming

Words and music by Charlotte G. Garman

1. Hal - low - een is com - ing, com - ing, com - ing,
2. There'll be lots of witch - es, witch - es, witch - es,

Hal - low - een is com - ing, oh, what fun!
There'll be lots of witch - es, oh, what fun!

Create other verses by substituting black cats, pumpkins, skeletons, etc., for witches. Repeat the first verse at the end of the song.

Key: C major
Starting tone: G
Autoharp introduction: CC/G7C
Beats per measure: 2/♩.

Over the River and through the Wood

Words by Lydia Maria Childs
Old Song

Have the children play the uneven rhythm of the horse's hooves on coconut shells, tone blocks, or the open ends of two paper cups ‖⅝ ♩ ♩♪ ♪ :‖

Add jingle bells on the accents of each measure: ‖⅝ ♩ ♩ ♩ ♩. :‖

Key: C major
Starting tone: C
Autoharp introduction: Omit Autoharp because of Fm chord.
Beats per measure: 2/♩.

Five Fat Turkeys

P. E. Peyce (Words adapted by David Stevens)

1. Five fat tur-keys are we, _____ We slept all night in a tree; _____
2. Five fat tur-keys are we, _____ We know you all will a - gree _____

When the cook came a--round, We could-n't be found, _____
That it cer-tain-ly pays On Thanks-giv-ing Days, _____

And that's why we're here. you see! _____
To sleep in the tall - est tree! _____

Help the children dramatize the story as they sing the song.

Key: G major
Starting tone: D
Autoharp introduction: GGGG/
Beats per measure: 4/♩

Little Pilgrims

Words by Louise B. Scott
Music by Lucille F. Wood

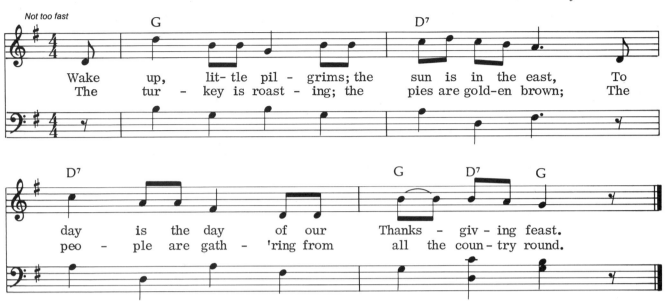

Not too fast

Wake up, lit- tle pil - grims; the sun is in the east, To
The tur - key is roast - ing; the pies are gold-en brown; The

day is the day of our Thanks - giv - ing feast.
peo - ple are gath - 'ring from all the coun-try round.

156

Wind through the Olive Trees

Key: G major
Starting tone: D
Autoharp introduction: GGG/GGG
Beats per measure: 3/♩

Traditional Carol

1. Wind through the ol - ive trees Soft - ly did blow,

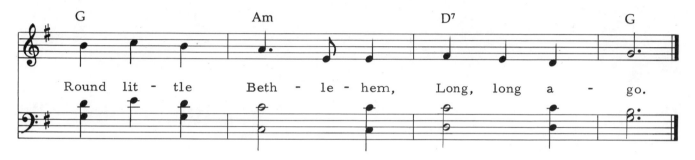

Round lit - tle Beth - le - hem, Long, long a - go.

2. Sheep on the hillside lay Whiter than snow.
   Shepherds were watching them, Long, long ago.

3. Then from the starry skies Angels bent low,
   Singing their songs of joy, Long, long ago.

4. For in a manger bed Long, long ago,
   Christ came to Bethlehem, Long, long ago.

Help the children experiment with different dynamic levels on each verse of the song.

Santa's Elves

Key: G major
Starting tone: G
Autoharp introduction: GG/D₇G
Beats per measure: 2/♩.

Words and music by Charlotte G. Garman

Not too slow

1. We are bus - y lit - tle elves, Mak - ing toys for San-ta's shelves,

We are bus - y lit - tle elves, Work - ing all the day.

2. Hammer, hammer, rap-a-tap, Bells a-ringing on our caps,
   Hammer, hammer, rap-a-tap, Working all the day.

Help the children make up additional verses. Use ideas such as painting, sewing, and carving. Motivate the children to dance like elves when the day's work is done.

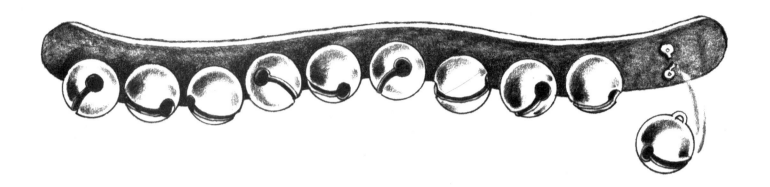

Key: C major
Starting tone: C
Autoharp introduction: C/C/G₇/C
Beats per measure: 3/♩

Ten Little Jingle Bells

Words and music by Virginia Pavelko

Brightly

1. Ten lit - tle jin - gle bells hung in a row, Ten lit - tle
2. One lit - tle jin - gle bell fell in the snow, Nine lit - tle

jin - gle bells helped the horse go. Mer - ri - ly, mer - ri - ly
jin - gle bells helped the horse go.

o - ver the snow, Mer - ri - ly, mer - ri - ly sleigh - ing we go.

Last verse slowly:
> One little jingle bell fell in the snow,
> No little jingle bells help the horse go.
> Slowly, so slowly the bells are all gone.
> We'll get some new ones and put them right on.

Original Chorus: Brightly

After the children sing the second verse and chorus, have them repeat the words and music, substituting the word "eight" for "nine." Follow the same procedure for the remaining numbers through "two"; then have the children sing the last verse. Select ten children to represent ten jingle bells. Have each child in turn sit down at the words "One little jingle bell fell in the snow."

Key: G major
Starting tone: D
Autoharp introduction: DD/DD
Beats per measure: 2/♩

Magic Time

Words by Louise B. Scott
Music by Lucille F. Wood

Merrily, with a running rhythm

On Christ-mas Eve does San - ta pack A mil - lion toys in -
On Christ-mas Eve can rein - deer fly To car - ry San - ta
On Christ-mas Eve does San - ta creep Right down the chim - ney

side his sack? Oh, yes, it's so! Oh, yes, it's
through the sky? Oh, yes, it's so! Oh, yes, it's
while I sleep? Oh, yes, it's so! Oh, yes, it's

so! It is a mag - ic time, you know.
so! It is a mag - ic time, you know.
so! It is a mag - ic time, you know.

Have various groups of children sing the questions of the song and other groups sing the answers.

Key: F major
Starting tone: C
Autoharp introduction: FF/FF
Beats per measure: 2/♩

Jingle Bells

J. S. Pierpoint

Verse *Happily*

Dash - ing through the snow, —— In a one-horse o - pen sleigh, ——

O'er the fields we go, —— Laugh-ing all the way. ——————

Bells on bob-tail ring, ———————— Mak - ing spi - rits bright, ———

What fun it is to ride and sing a sleigh-ing song to - night. Oh!

Refrain

Jin - gle bells, —— jin - gle bells, —— jin - gle all the way, ——————

Oh, what fun it is to ride in a one-horse o - pen sleigh; ___

Jin - gle bells, ___ jin - gle bells, ___ jin - gle all the way, ___.

Oh, what fun it is to ride in a one-horse o - pen sleigh. ___

Have the children use rhythm instruments for sound effects in this song. They can emphasize the difference in the verse and the refrain by using temple blocks, coconut shells, or open ends of two paper cups for a horse's "clip clop" on the verse and by using jingle bells on the refrain.

Key: G major
Starting tone: B
Autoharp introduction: GG/D₇G
Beats per measure: 2/♩

Jolly Old Saint Nicholas

Traditional

1. Jol - ly old Saint Nich - o - las, Lean your ear this way!____

Don't you tell a sin - gle soul What I'm going to say;____

Christ-mas Eve is com - ing soon; Now you dear old man,____

Whis-per what you'll bring to me;__ Tell me if you can. __

2. When the clock is striking twelve, When I'm fast asleep,
   Down the chimney broad and black, With your pack you'll creep;
   All the stockings you will find Hanging in a row;
   Mine will be the shortest one; You'll be sure to know.

3. Johnny wants a pair of skates; Susy wants a dolly;
   Nelly wants a story book; She thinks dolls are folly;
   As for me, my dear old friend, When you come tonight;
   Bring for me, dear Santa Claus What you think is right.

It would be challenging to assign a rhythm instrument to each of the three rhythm patterns of the song. When the children are familiar with the song, have them play each instrument as they sing that pattern:

Rhythm sticks:

Jingle bells:

Triangle:

The pattern for each phrase of the song would be like this:

sticks   jingle bells   sticks   triangle

162

Key: G major
Starting tone: D
Autoharp introduction: GGG/GGG
Beats per measure: 3/♩

We Wish You a Merry Christmas

Traditional English Carol

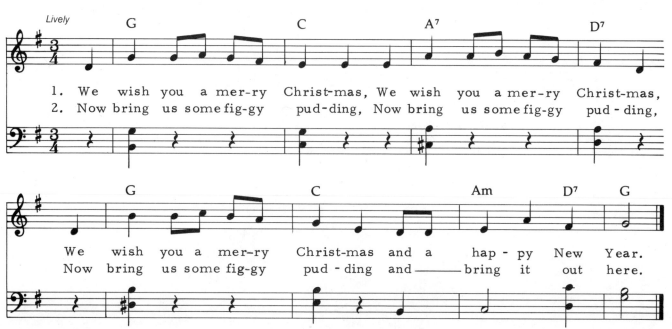

1. We wish you a mer-ry Christ-mas, We wish you a mer-ry Christ-mas,
2. Now bring us some fig-gy pud-ding, Now bring us some fig-gy pud-ding,

We wish you a mer-ry Christ-mas and a hap-py New Year.
Now bring us some fig-gy pud-ding and——bring it out here.

3. We won't go until we get some, We won't go until we get some,
   We won't go until we get some, So bring it out here.

Encourage the children to create various patterns of stamping, clapping, or slapping thighs or arms to feel the strong one-two-three of the underlying beat.

Key: C major
Starting tone: G
Autoharp introduction: CCCC/
Beats per measure: 4/♩

My Dreydl

Words by S. S. Grossman
Music by S. E. Goldfarb

1. I have a lit-tle drey-dl, I made it out of clay;
And when it's dry and read-y, Then drey-dl I shall play.
O drey-dl, drey-dl, drey-dl, I made it out of clay;
O drey-dl, drey-dl, drey-dl, Now drey-dl I shall play.

2. It has a lovely body, With leg so short and thin;
And when it is all tired, It drops and then I win.
O dreydl, dreydl, dreydl, With leg so short and thin;
O dreydl, dreydl, dreydl, It drops and then I win.

A dreydl is a four-sided top. It has special Hebrew letters on each of the four sides. Jewish children enjoy playing with their dreydls during Hanukkah, or the Festival of Lights.

Help the children play the last measure of each phrase on the bells:

1 and 3   2 and 4

164

Key: F major
Starting tone: F
Autoharp introduction: FF/C₇F
Beats per measure: 4/♩

Two Little Valentines
Words and music by Charlotte G. Garman

Not too fast

Two lit-tle val-en-tines came one day, While I was run-ning out-side to play.

One was pret-ty and cov-ered with lace, One had a sil - ly fun - ny face.

Call the children's attention to the syllables in the song that are sung on more than one note. Let them practice singing these out of context, so that they can sing these syllables rhythmically in the song.

Key: F major
Starting tone: C
Autoharp introduction: FFFFFF/
Beats per measure: 6/♪

Valentines Red
Words and music by George K. Evans

Gaily

mp

Val - en - tines red, val - en - tines white, All say-ing, "I love you."

Here's one for John, here's one for Jane, One for our teach - er, too.

Ask the children to substitute the names of any children in the class each time they sing the song. This melodic pattern occurs four times:

The pattern could be played on the bells as an introduction, each time the children sing it in the song, and as a coda.

From *Growing with Music Book 1 Related Arts Edition* by Harry R. Wilson, Walter Ehret, Alice M. Knuth, Edward J. Hermann, Albert A. Renna © 1970 by Prentice-Hall, Inc., Englewood Cliffs, N.J. Reprinted by permission.

Key: F major
Starting tone: C
Autoharp introduction: FF/C₇F
Beats per measure: 2/♩

Hallelu

German Folk Tune

Joyfully

Hal-le - lu, hal-le-lu, hal-le - lu, hal-le-lu - jah, Praise to the Lord. Praise to the Lord, Hal - le - lu - jah, Praise to the Lord, Hal - le - lu - jah, Praise to the Lord, Hal - le - lu - jah, Praise to the Lord.

German:
Hallelu, hallelu, hallelu, halleluia, Preiset den Herrn.
Preiset den Herrn, Halleluia, Preiset den Herrn, Halleluia
Preiset den Herrn, Halleluia, Preiset den Herrn.

Divide the class in half. Ask one group to sing only the words "Hallelu" throughout the song and the second group to sing only the words "Praise to the Lord."
This song is especially fun to sing if the children stand only when it's their turn to sing. All may join in on the final phrase.

166

My Own Dear Land

Pledge of Allegiance

I pledge allegiance to the flag
of the United States of America
and to the republic for which it stands,
one nation, under God, indivisible,
with liberty and justice for all.

Francis Bellamy

Key: F major
Starting tone: C
Autoharp introduction: FFFFFF/
Beats per measure: 6/♪

Home on the Range

Traditional Cowboy Song

Verse

Easily

Oh, give me a home where the buf-fa-lo roam,

Where the deer and the an-te-lope play, _____

Where sel-dom is heard a dis-cour-ag-ing word,

And the skies are not cloud-y all day. _____

Refrain

Home, home on the range, _____
Where the deer and the an - te - lope play, _____
Where sel - dom is heard a dis - cour - ag - ing word,
And the skies are not cloud - y all day. _____

One of the most challenging aspects of this song for little children is holding or sustaining those notes which should be sustained: play, day, range, play, day. They are all held for five counts. The "day" at the end of the verse is held for five counts with an eigth rest. Help the children count beats by strumming each beat on the Autoharp or guitar or by letting the children tap the beats with their feet. Help them understand that "range" is sustained on the vowel sound.

Key: D minor
Starting tone: G
Autoharp introduction: The Autoharp is not used.
Beats per measure: 3/♩ (4/♩, 2/♩)

Indian Lullaby

Miwok Indian

1. Sleep, my lit-tle one! Sleep, my lit - tle one! my lit - tle squir-rel!
2. Sleep, my lit-tle one! Sleep, my lit - tle one! my lit - tle crick - et!
3. Sleep, my lit-tle one! Sleep, my lit - tle one! my lit - tle lin - net!

Safe in the tree - tops the squir-rels are sleep - ing.
Safe in the tree - tops the crick - ets are sleep - ing.
Safe in the tree - tops the lin - nets are sleep - ing.

All are a - sleep in their bas-kets of wil - low.

This song is a lullaby of the Miwok Indians, who lived in the Yosemite region of California. The linnet mentioned in the song is a small bird.

A soft drumbeat may be played on the underlying beat of the song.

170

Key: G major
Starting tone: G
Autoharp introduction: GG/D₇G
Beats per measure: 2/♩

Traditional Song

Verse

Yan - kee Doo - dle came to town A - rid - ing on a po - ny,

He stuck a feath - er in his hat And called it mac - a - ro - ni.

Refrain

Yan - kee Doo - dle keep it up, Yan - kee Doo - dle dan - dy,

Mind the mu - sic and the step, And with the girls be han - dy.

2. Father and I went down to camp, Along with Captain Goodwin,
   And there we saw the men and boys, As thick as hasty pudding.
   Refrain:
3. There was Captain Washington, Upon a slapping stallion,
   A-giving orders to his men; I guess there was a million.
   Refrain:

Help the children become aware of the two sections of this song: the verse and the refrain. The melodic rhythm of the verse is mostly even, while the melodic rhythm of the refrain is mostly uneven. Let them clap, tap, or play these two different rhythm patterns on different instruments, one during the verse and another during the refrain.

Key: F major
Starting tone: F
Autoharp introduction: FFF/FFF
Beats per measure: 3/♩

America

Words by Samuel Francis Smith
Music by Henry Carey

My coun-try 'tis of thee, Sweet land of lib-er-ty,

Of thee I sing. Land where my fa-thers died!

Land of the Pil-grims' pride! From ev-'ry moun-tain-side,

Let free-dom ring.

Key: G major
Starting tone: G
Autoharp introduction: $G/G/G_7/G_7$
Beats per measure: $2/\quarternote$

This Land Is Your Land

Words and music by Woody Guthrie

Moderately bright

This land is your land, ____ this land is my land ____ From Cal-i-for-nia ____ to the New York is-land, ____ From the red-wood for-est ____ to the Gulf Stream wa-ters; ____ This land was made for you and me. ____

Have the children clap the underlying beat as they sing this song.

Key: G major
Starting tone: D
Autoharp introduction: G/G/D₇/G
Beats per measure: 2/♩

You're a Grand Old Flag

Words and music by George M. Cohan

mf You're a grand old flag, you're a high fly - ing flag, and for - e - ver in peace may you wave; _____ You're the em - blem of the land I love, The home of the free and the brave. Ev - 'ry heart beats true, un - der Red, White, and Blue; Where there's nev - er a boast or brag; _____ But should

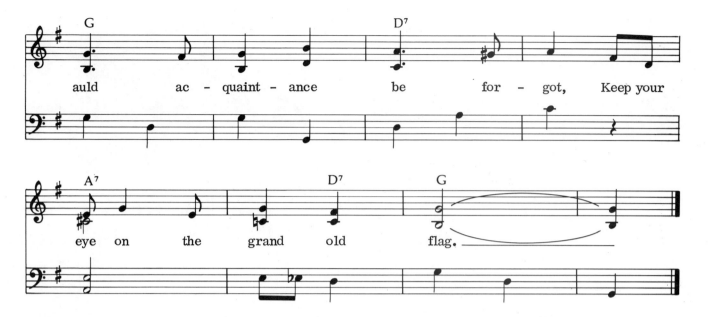

auld ac - quaint - ance be for - got, Keep your eye on the grand old flag. ____

Have groups of children take turns marching around the room to this song, while the others watch the parade and wave real or imaginary flags in time to the music.

Three Cheers for the Red, White, and Blue

Adapted by Charlotte G. Garman

Key: F major
Starting tone: E
Autoharp introduction: FF/C₇F
Beats per measure: 4/♩

Three ——— cheers for the red, white, and blue. ———

Three ——— cheers for the red, white, and blue, ———

The ——— star - span - gled ban - ner for - ev - er, ———

Three ——— cheers —— for the red, white, and blue. ———

Have the children march around the room to this song. Ask them to take turns carrying the flag and playing a drum on the accents and sticks on the underlying beat:

Drum:

Sticks:

Key: G minor
Starting tone: D
Autoharp introduction: Gm Gm Gm Gm/
Beats per measure: 4/♩

America, I Love You So

Words by Patricia Haglund Nielsen
Old English Tune

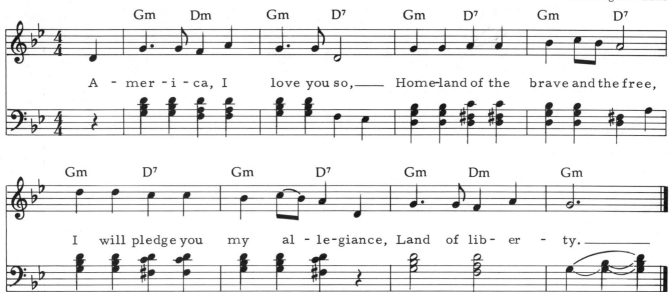

A - mer - i - ca, I love you so,___ Home-land of the brave and the free,

I will pledge you my al - le-giance, Land of lib - er - ty.___

Suggested bell or piano ostinato:  Keep repeating.

Have some of the children sing this vocal ostinato over and over while the others sing the song:

A - mer - i - ca, A - mer - i - ca

Key: B♭ major (C major)
Starting tone: D (E)
Autoharp introduction: (CC/G₇C) See below.
Beats per measure: 4/♩

There Are Many Flags

Words by M. H. Howliston
Traditional

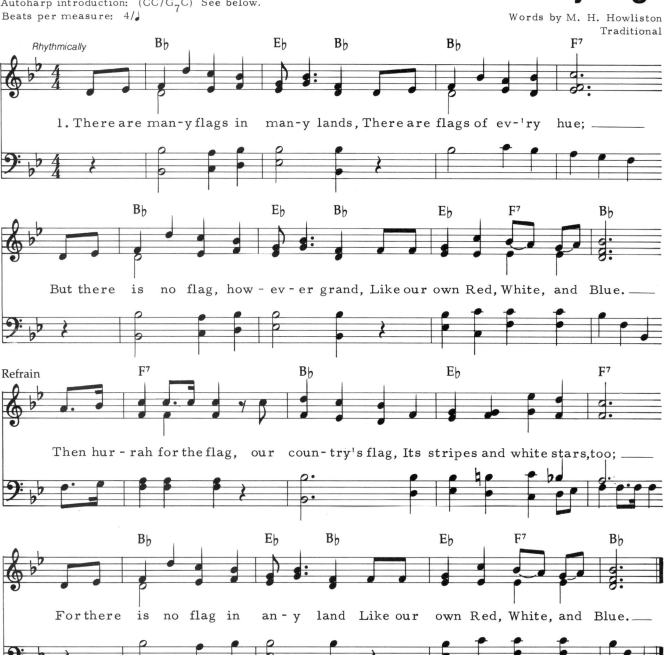

Rhythmically

1. There are man-y flags in man-y lands, There are flags of ev-'ry hue; _____

But there is no flag, how-ev-er grand, Like our own Red, White, and Blue. _____

Refrain

Then hur-rah for the flag, our coun-try's flag, Its stripes and white stars, too; _____

For there is no flag in an-y land Like our own Red, White, and Blue. _____

2. We shall always love the stars and stripes, And we ever shall be true
    To this land of ours and the dear old flag, Just our own Red, White, and Blue. Refrain:

Of the four phrases in this song, two are exactly alike (two, four), three are similar (one, two, four), and one is different. Help the children find the ones that are the same, similar, and different. Let them emphasize the similarities by singing phrase one, *piano;* phrase two, *piano* with a crescendo; phrase three, *forte;* and phrase four, *piano* with a crescendo.

Key: F major
Starting tone: C
Autoharp introduction: FFFF/
Beats per measure: 4/♩

My Own Dear Country

German Folk Song

Respectfully

I pledge my-self faith-ful, with heart and with hand, ____

To thee my own dear coun-try, to thee my na-tive land, ____

To thee my own dear coun-try, to thee my na-tive land. ____

This is a good song to sing just before or just after saying the Pledge of Allegiance. Encourage the children to sing with full singing (not yelling) voices.

Ring around the World

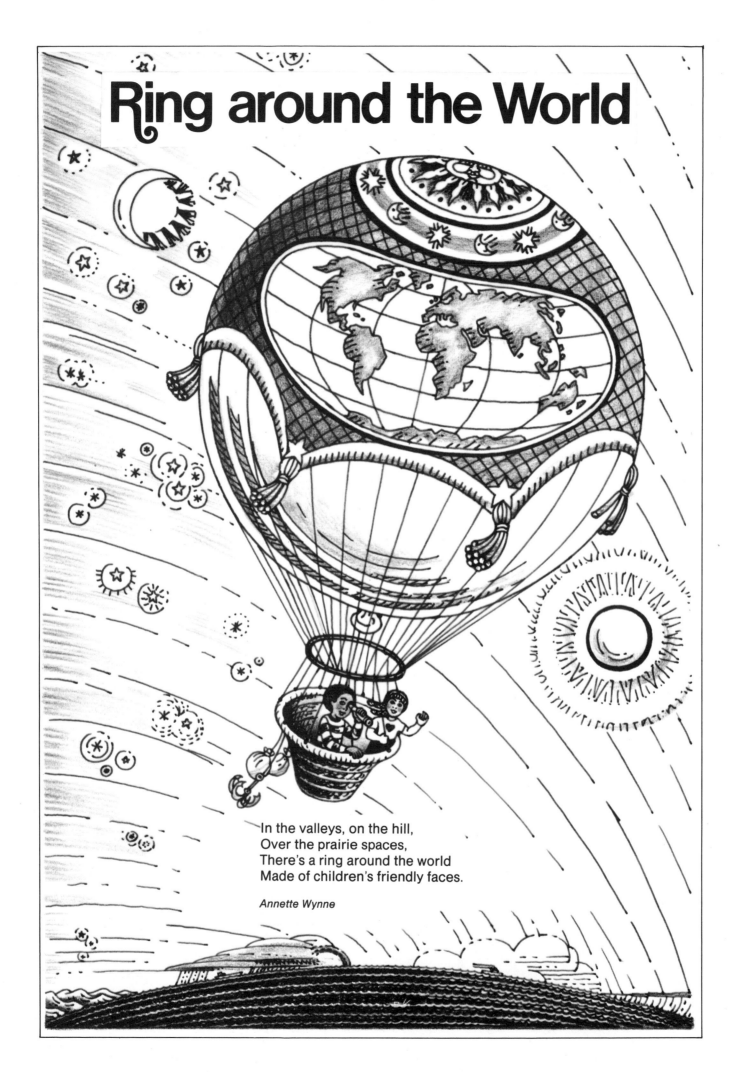

In the valleys, on the hill,
Over the prairie spaces,
There's a ring around the world
Made of children's friendly faces.

Annette Wynne

Key: C major
Starting tone: E
Autoharp introduction: CCCC/
Beats per measure: 4/♩

Three Doves

Traditional (Italian)

Con gracia

1. In the sky, __ three doves __ are fly-ing __ In the sky, __ three doves __ are fly-ing __ In the sky, __ three doves are fly-ing __ Hear their haunt-ing cry, hear their haunt-ing cry, hear their haunt-ing cry.

2. O'er the sea the doves are going, (3 times)
   To a land they know. (3 times)

3. On white wings the doves are soaring, (3 times)
   To return no more. (3 times)

As you sing this Italian folk song with the children, use graceful, rhythmic arm motions and have the children imitate them. Begin the first verse with arms held out to the sides. Slowly move your arms forward and back again in time to the music. For the second verse, move your arms together from side to side so that your hands trace a figure eight. For the third verse, place your arms over your head and bring each hand down in front of you so that your hands trace the two halves of a circle.

From *Growing with Music Book 7 Related Arts Edition* by Harry R. Wilson, Walter Ehret, Alice M. Knuth, Edward J. Hermann, Albert A. Renna, first edition © 1966 by Prentice-Hall, Inc., Englewood Cliffs, New Jersey. Adapted and reprinted with permission.

Key: C major
Starting tone: C
Autoharp introduction: CC/G_7C
Beats per measure: 4/♩

Who's That?

American Folk Song

Who's that tap-ping at the win-dow? Who's that knock-ing at the door?

Su - sie tap-ping at the win - dow, Da - vid knock-ing at the door.
An - gie Will - ie

Have the children dramatize this American folk song. Suggest that they take turns singing the questions and answers and that they use their own names for the answers.

Eskimo Dance Song

MacKenzie River Eskimos
Melody adapted

Key: F pentatonic
Starting tone: C
Autoharp introduction: The Autoharp is not used.
Beats per measure: 2/♩

Ye - ye - e. My arms they wave high in the air,

My hands they flut - ter be - hind my head; They wave a -

bove my head like the wings of a bird. Let me dance and

shrug __ my shoul - ders. My arms, let me fold them,

let me crouch down, Fold my hands un - der my

chin. E - e - e.

Encourage the children to perform the motions indicated by the words of this Eskimo song. They may form a circle and take short, shuffling steps as they sing and do the motions.

183

Key: F pentatonic
Starting tone: C
Autoharp introduction: The Autoharp is not used。
Beats per measure: 2/♩

Little Baby Chicks

Translation by Amy Yamaguchi
Japanese Children's Song

Lit - tle ba - by chicks, Lit - tle yel - low feet are hop - ping here and hop - ping there, Lit - tle yel - low feet are hop - ping ev - 'ry-where. Lit - tle yel - low feet run a-way and hide. Peek - a - boo, I see you!

Suggest that the children dramatize this Japanese children's song. Some of them may pretend to be baby chicks, while others pretend to be children playing peekaboo with the chicks.

184

Key: G minor
Starting tone: D
Autoharp introduction: GmGm/GmGm
Beats per measure: 2/♩

The Birch Tree

Translation by Jacob Robbins
Traditional (Russian)

1. Lit - tle birch tree grow - ing in the mead - ow,

Cur - ly leaved and grow - ing in the mead - ow,

Liu - lee, liu - lee, in the mead - ow,

Liu - lee, liu - lee in the mead - ow.

Sing each verse line below twice. For the chorus,
repeat the words in italics.

2. Who will break your fresh white branches *in the meadow*.
3. I'll go out a-walking *in the meadow*.
4. I will break your branches *in the meadow*.
5. I will cut three branches *in the meadow*.

6. I will make three whistles *in the meadow*.
7. I will take my singing *balalaika*.
8. Play a song upon my *balalaika*.

Accompany this Russian folk song by striking a triangle at the beginning of each phrase.

185

Key: G major
Starting tone: D
Autoharp introduction: GG/D₇G
Beats per measure: 2/♩

Hush, Little Baby

Southern Folk Song

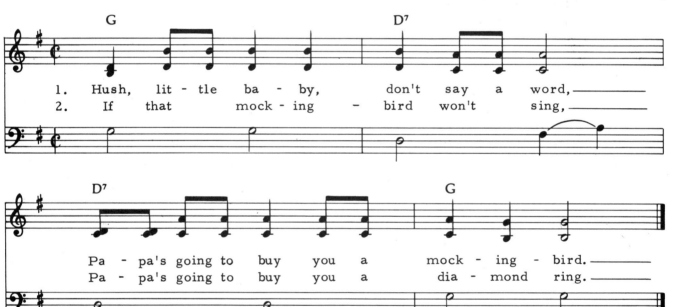

1. Hush, lit - tle ba - by, don't say a word,——
2. If that mock - ing - bird won't sing,——

Pa - pa's going to buy you a mock - ing - bird.——
Pa - pa's going to buy you a dia - mond ring.——

3. If that diamond ring turns brass,
   Papa's going to buy you a looking glass.
4. If that looking glass gets broke,
   Papa's going to buy you a billy goat.
5. If that billy goat won't pull,
   Papa's going to buy you a cart and bull.
6. If that cart and bull turn over,
   Papa's going to buy you a dog named Rover.
7. If that dog named Rover won't bark,
   Papa's going to buy you a horse and cart.
8. If that horse and cart break down,
   We'll take a walk all around the town.

Suggested vocal or bell ostinato to be used as an accompaniment:

keep repeating

Hush, lit - tle ba - by, Hush, lit - tle ba - by.

186

Key: D major
Starting tone: D
Autoharp introduction: DD/DD
Beats per measure: 2/♩

Green Rose Hula

Words adapted by Roberta McLaughlin
As sung by Hawaiian students

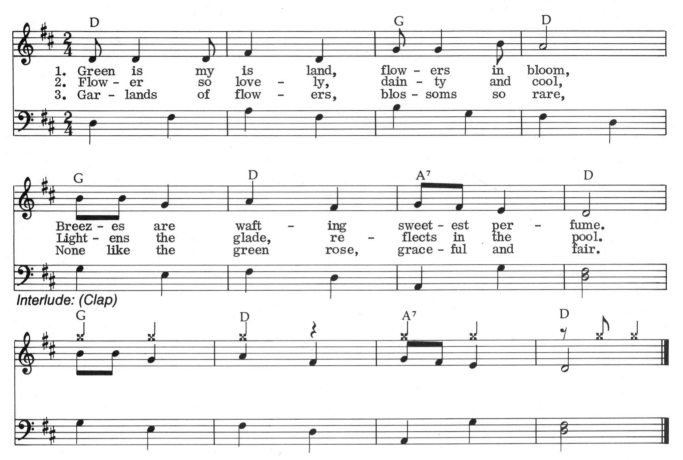

1. Green is my is - land, flow - ers in bloom,
2. Flow - er so love - ly, dain - ty and cool,
3. Gar - lands of flow - ers, blos - soms so rare,

Breez - es are waft - ing sweet - est per - fume.
Light - ens the glade, re - flects in the pool.
None like the green rose, grace - ful and fair.

Interlude: (Clap)

During the interlude, have the children clap or play rhythm instruments as indicated.

GLOSSARY

Accent

In music, a beat that is stressed more than others. The first beat in a measure usually receives an accent.

Coda

An ending passage, often instrumental, added at the conclusion of a song or other composition.

D.C. al Fine

A direction that requires a performer to repeat a composition from the beginning and to stop at the indication *Fine.*

D.S. al Fine

A direction that requires a performer to repeat a composition from the sign (𝄋) and to stop at the indication *Fine.*

Dynamic Symbols and Terms

pp	pianissimo	very soft
p	piano	soft
mp	mezzo piano	medium soft
mf	mezzo forte	medium loud
f	forte	loud
ff	fortissimo	very loud

Fine

A direction marking the stopping place after the music has been repeated.

Interlude

A passage played between other sections, as a percussion interlude between two verses of a song.

Introduction

A passage, usually instrumental, that sets the mood, tempo, and key before a song begins.

Legato

Smooth and connected; in a flowing manner, as from tone to tone in a melody.

Marcato

With each note accented.

Melodic Rhythm

The rhythm of the individual notes of the melody as opposed to the underlying beat.

Ostinato

A brief rhythmic or melodic pattern that is repeated over and over as an accompaniment.

Pentatonic Scale

A five-tone scale that is the basis of much Oriental, African, American Indian, and other folk music. It corresponds to five consecutive black keys of the piano keyboard or to tones 1, 2, 3, 5, and 6 of any major scale.

Phrase

A musical thought or sentence of variable length, often four measures long. Many of the songs in this book are printed with one line of music for each phrase.

Refrain

In a verse-refrain song, the part that is repeated between the verses.

Repeat Signs

A single repeat sign (:‖) indicates that the music is to be repeated from the beginning. A pair of repeat signs (‖:   :‖) indicate that the music between them is to be repeated.

Ritard

To become gradually slower in tempo.

Staccato

In a crisply detached manner.

Tempo

The relative rate of speed of a song or other composition.

Underlying Beat

The regular pulse of a song, usually indicated by the meter signature.

2/4 one strong and one weak pulse per measure

3/4 three pulses per measure: strong, weak, weak

4/4 four pulses per measure: strong, weak, half-strong, weak

6/8 six pulses per measure: strong, weak, weak, half-strong, weak, weak (In rapid tempo, only two pulses per measure are felt, the strong and the half-strong.)

CLASSIFIED INDEX

TRANSPORTATION

TUNES WITH AUTOHARP ACCOMPANIMENT

One Chord
14, 62, 142, 143b

Two Chords
2, 11, 24, 25, 29, 32a, 33, 48, 50, 57, 58, 60, 61a, 61b, 66, 68b, 69, 71, 76, 90, 98, 99, 101, 102, 112, 120, 122, 124, 125, 127, 130b, 131, 132, 134, 137, 139, 145, 146a, 146b, 153a, 153b, 156, 158, 164, 181, 182, 185, 186

Three Chords
5, 6, 7, 8, 9, 10, 12, 13, 15, 17, 18, 22, 28, 32b, 39, 46, 49, 51, 52, 53a, 53b, 54, 55, 56, 63, 64, 65a, 65b, 70, 72, 73, 74, 77, 78, 79, 82, 83, 86, 87, 88, 89, 94, 95, 96, 97, 100, 108, 113, 114, 116, 118, 123, 128, 130a, 133, 138, 140, 141, 144, 147, 148, 150, 152, 157b, 159, 165a, 171, 172, 177, 178, 179, 187

Four or More Chords
3, 16, 19, 23, 26, 30, 34, 36, 37, 38, 40, 44, 68a, 84, 85, 92, 107, 110, 136, 149, 154, 157a, 159, 160, 162, 163, 165b, 166, 168, 173, 174, 176

ALPHABETICAL INDEX

2 3 4 5 6 7 8 9 10 11 12 13 14 15 — B — 91 90 89 88 87 86 85 84 83 82